Course 1

MOVING MATH FORWARD THROUGH CRITICAL THINKING AND EXPLORATION

# Fraction Times

## Focusing on Multiplication and Division of Fractions and Decimals

Linda Jensen Sheffield

Suzanne H. Chapin

M. Katherine Gavin

Kendall Hunt
publishing company

# ACKNOWLEDGMENTS

## Math Innovations Writing Team

### Authors

Linda Jensen Sheffield

Suzanne H. Chapin

M. Katherine Gavin

### Project Manager

Janice M. Vuolo

### Teacher Edition Team

Alice J. Gabbard

Jacob J. Whitmore

Ann Marie Spinelli

### Writing Assistants

Jane Paulin

Kathy Dorkin

### Mathematics Editor

Kathleen G. Snook

### Assessment Specialist

Nancy Anderson

### Advisory Board

Jerry P. Becker

Janet Beissinger

Diane J. Briars

Ann Lawrence

Ira J. Papick

Cover photo of model with vegetables by TSI Graphics. Other images on cover used under license by ShutterStock, Inc. Unless otherwise noted, photos in this book used under license by Shutterstock, Inc.

# Kendall Hunt

publishing company

www.kendallhunt.com

Send all inquiries to:

4050 Westmark Drive

Dubuque, IA 52004-1840

1-800-542-6657

Production Date: 8/14/2014

Printed by: King Printing Co., Inc.

Lowell, Massachusetts

United States of America

Batch number: 426702

# Fraction Times
## Focusing on Multiplication and Division of Fractions and Decimals

# Table of Contents

# UNIT GOALS

## Fraction Times: Focusing on Multiplication and Division of Fractions and Decimals

After studying this unit, you should be able to:

- Mentally multiply and divide decimals and fractions by powers of ten.

- Write and solve single- and multi-step problems.

- Draw diagrams to explain multiplication and division of fractions, mixed numbers and decimals.

- Describe algorithms for multiplying fractions and mixed numbers.

- Explain how to multiply and divide fractions and why your method works.

- Explain algorithms for multiplying and dividing decimals. Be able to give examples of their use.

- Multiply and divide fractions and decimals mentally, with paper and pencil and with a calculator. Be able to make reasonable estimates of the results of these operations.

# Dear Student Mathematician,

Business owners and teachers often say that working with fractions and decimals is one of the most important things students can learn. You have to understand fractions and decimals to work with money, make measurements, and perform a variety of other tasks. Estimation and fluency with computation is also important.

In this unit, *Fractions Times: Focusing on Multiplication and Division of Fractions and Decimals,* you will strengthen your understanding of multiplication and division of rational numbers. You will make connections among rational numbers, models and diagrams, algorithms, equations and applications. As you do this, you will connect multiplication to addition as well as to the inverse operation of division and to subtraction. You will also connect what you have learned about multiplying and dividing whole numbers to multiplying and dividing proper and improper fractions, mixed numbers and decimals.

We hope that you enjoy the activities involving multiplication and division of rational numbers in this unit. A deep understanding of multiplication and division of rational numbers should prepare you well for your future.

Mathematically yours,
The Authors

*Linda Sheffield*

*Suzanne H. Chapin*

*M. Katherine Gavin*

# SECTION 1

# Multiplying Fractions

Books from long ago can tell us much about life in those days. Problems in old math books give a glimpse of everyday life. They also tell us how students thought about mathematics. In this section, you will explore problems involving multiplication of fractions and mixed numbers, beginning with some problems written over 100 years ago. You will find the answers, the products, as well as investigate the numbers being multiplied.

## LESSON 1.1  Multiplying Fractions and Whole Numbers

► product

 Start It Off

One interpretation of $12 \cdot 8 = 96$ is that 12 groups of 8 objects is equal to 96 objects.

1. In this way, $12 \cdot 4 = 48$ means _____.

   Copy and finish the following pattern:

   $12 \cdot 8 = 96$

   $12 \cdot 4 = 48$

   $12 \cdot 2 = $ _____

   $12 \cdot$ _____ $= $ _____

   $12 \cdot \frac{1}{2} = $ _____

   $12 \cdot$ _____ $= $ _____

2. How would you interpret your last equation as repeated groups?

3. What equation would come next in this pattern?

Luke found an old math book from 1878 in a used bookstore. He liked reading the problems about everyday life. One of the first problems he noticed was, "If a man can earn $\$\frac{3}{10}$ per hour, how much can he earn in 5 hours?"

**1.** Luke thought it was interesting that the hourly wage was written as $\$\frac{3}{10}$.

   **a)** How is $\$\frac{3}{10}$ usually written?

   **b)** If a man earned $\$\frac{3}{10}$ per hour, estimate how much he would earn in 5 hours. Is this more than $1.00? Is it more than $2.00?

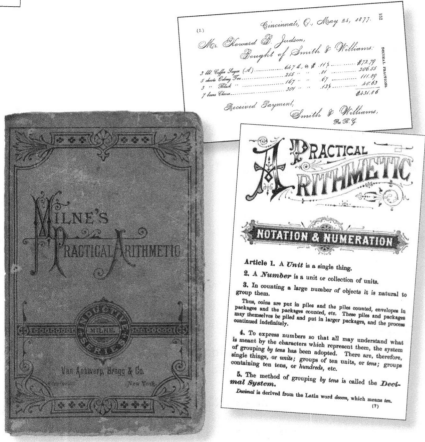

Luke earns $8 per hour babysitting. Suppose Luke babysits for 5 hours.

2. Write both an addition equation and a multiplication equation to show the total amount Luke earns. Is it faster to find the total by adding or by multiplying?

3. Write an equation to show what a man in 1878 would earn in 5 hours at $\$\frac{3}{10}$ per hour. Talk to a partner about how you might solve your equation.

4. There are many ways you might find the man's earnings.

   a) Write $\$\frac{3}{10}$ as 30¢ and find his earnings by writing and solving an addition problem.

   b) Write $\$\frac{3}{10}$ as $0.30 and find his earnings by writing and solving a multiplication problem.

   c) Do you prefer using multiplication or addition? Why?

   d) Leave $\$\frac{3}{10}$ as a fraction and use a number line to find his earnings. How does this method compare to the methods in Parts a and b?

   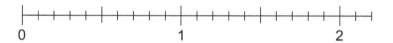

   e) When you multiplied $5 \cdot \frac{3}{10}$, how many tenths did you get as an answer? What is this as a simplified mixed number?

5. Suppose the man got a large raise and made $\$\frac{3}{4}$ per hour.

   a) How much would he earn in 7 hours? Show your solution on the number line.

   b) $7 \cdot \frac{3}{4} = \frac{?}{4}$ Write this product as a mixed number and compare to your answer on the number line.

   c) Make up your own problem about earning money with an hourly wage less than $1. Trade your problem with a partner and solve. Write your answer as a fraction. Convert to a simplified mixed number if the product is greater than 1.

6. Write a general rule for multiplying a whole number and a fraction.

7. To get to work, a man walked $\frac{2}{3}$ mile each day. He also had to walk $\frac{2}{3}$ mile to get home each evening.

   a) Use the number line to show how far the man walked in one day. Write your answer as an improper fraction and as a mixed number.

   ```
   |++|++|++|++|++|
   0   1   2   3   4
   ```

   b) Complete the chart to show how far the man walked to get to work and back in his six-day workweek.

| Days | 1 | 2 | 3 | 4 | 5 | 6 |
|------|---|---|---|---|---|---|
| Total Miles Walked | $\frac{4}{3} = 1\frac{?}{3}$ | $\frac{?}{3} = 2\frac{?}{3}$ | | | | |

   c) Kayla wrote $6 \cdot 1\frac{1}{3}$ for the total miles for six days. She said that she could take $(6 \cdot 1) + (6 \cdot \frac{1}{3})$. With a partner, decide if this would give the same answer as the one on your chart. What property says that $6 \cdot (1 + \frac{1}{3}) = (6 \cdot 1) + (6 \cdot \frac{1}{3})$? How is this similar to saying $6 \cdot 13 = 6 \cdot (10 + 3) = (6 \cdot 10) + (6 \cdot 3)$?

   d) Bart said that you could write $1\frac{1}{3}$ as $\frac{4}{3}$ and then multiply by 6. What improper fraction would Bart get for an answer? When he converts this to a mixed number, would he get the same answer as Kayla?

MATHEMATICALLY SPEAKING

▶ distributive property of multiplication over addition

The distributive property of multiplication over addition states that $a \cdot (b + c) = (a \cdot b) + (a \cdot c)$. Using the commutative property of multiplication, you can also say $(b + c) \cdot a = (b \cdot a) + (c \cdot a)$. This can be very useful in multiplying a whole number times a fraction.

Example

$$5 \cdot 2\frac{3}{4} = (5 \cdot 2) + (5 \cdot \frac{3}{4})$$
$$= 10 + \frac{15}{4}$$
$$= 10 + 3\frac{3}{4}$$
$$= 13\frac{3}{4}$$

8. In 2008, the minimum wage in some states was $\$7\frac{1}{4}$.

   a) Would it take more or less than 3 hours to earn $25 if you earned minimum wage?

   b) How much would a person earning minimum wage earn in 5 hours in 2008? Show your solution on a number line. How might you use the distributive property of multiplication over addition to help you solve this?

9. Find each product using the following two methods:

- Use the distributive property of multiplication over addition.

- Convert the mixed number to an improper fraction and multiply.

Compare your answers using the two different methods.

**a)**  $5 \cdot 2\frac{3}{4}$    **b)**  $3 \cdot 1\frac{5}{8}$    **c)**  $2 \cdot 3\frac{2}{3}$

10. Choose one of the expressions in Question 9 and find the product using a number line. Explain how to multiply a whole number and a mixed number using the distributive property of multiplication over addition.

## A New Look at Finding Parts

Luke's class is planning a spring party for the Bluebird Preschool. They are going to have an egg hunt. Luke thought, "If I have 4 dozen eggs, I have 4 groups of 12 eggs. I can multiply $4 \cdot 12$ to find the total number of eggs. If I have $\frac{1}{3}$ of one dozen eggs, I have a third of one group of 12 eggs. I can multiply $\frac{1}{3} \cdot 12$ to find the number of eggs I have."

**11.** How many eggs are there in $\frac{1}{3}$ of a dozen? How is this shown in the picture? How does this relate to multiplication?

**12.** How is $\frac{1}{4}$ of a dozen similar to finding $\frac{1}{4} \cdot 12$? How is this like $12 \div 4$?

**13.** With a partner, find the number of eggs in each part of a dozen.

   **a)** 6 dozen

   **b)** $\frac{1}{3}$ dozen

   **c)** $\frac{2}{3}$ dozen

   **d)** $\frac{1}{4}$ dozen

   **e)** $\frac{3}{4}$ dozen

   **f)** $1\frac{1}{2}$ dozen

**14.** The class is bringing peanuts and apple cider for the party. Each bag of peanuts weighs $\frac{2}{3}$ of a pound, and Todd brought 6 bags. Maureen bought 6 bottles of apple cider, but brought only $\frac{2}{3}$ of the bottles to the party.

   **a)** Todd wrote $6 \cdot \frac{2}{3} = p$ to show how many pounds of peanuts he brought for the party. Show this using a number line or other model. How many pounds of peanuts did Todd bring?

   **b)** Maureen wrote $\frac{2}{3} \cdot 6 = b$ to show how many bottles of cider she brought to the party. Draw a model to show this. How many bottles of cider did she bring?

   **c)** Compare $6 \cdot \frac{2}{3}$ and $\frac{2}{3} \cdot 6$. Are the models the same? Are the answers the same? How is this like comparing $6 \cdot 3$ and $3 \cdot 6$?

   **d)** Does the commutative property of multiplication hold for fractions? Explain.

   **e)** Does the rule you use to multiply a fraction times a whole number also work to multiply a whole number times a fraction? Demonstrate using $6 \cdot \frac{2}{3}$ and $\frac{2}{3} \cdot 6$.

**15.** Monica brought 48 muffins to the party. The 14 boys and 10 girls at the party want to share them equally.

   **a)** What fraction of the preschool class are boys? What fraction are girls?

   **b)** What fraction of the total muffins should the boys get? How many muffins should the boys get? Explain in words and pictures.

16. Luke's class polled the 24 children at the party on their favorite places to visit. Luke made this graph to show the results.

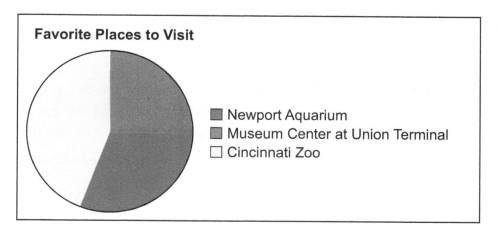

**Favorite Places to Visit**

- Newport Aquarium
- Museum Center at Union Terminal
- Cincinnati Zoo

a) Estimate the fraction of the children who chose the Newport Aquarium. How might you find this fraction of 24 children? How many groups would you break 24 into?

b) $\frac{5}{12}$ of the children chose the zoo. How many children chose the zoo?

c) What fraction of the children chose the Museum Center? How many children is that?

d) Does the rule you developed for multiplying a fraction times a whole number work for $\frac{5}{12} \cdot 24$?

 Think Beyond

e) Is there an easier way to multiply $\frac{5}{12} \cdot 24$? Can you first multiply $5 \cdot 24$ and then put that over the denominator as $\frac{5 \cdot 24}{12}$? Explain.

 **rap It Up**

a) How is multiplication of a fraction by a whole number like repeated addition? Use $8 \cdot \frac{3}{4}$ as an example. Include a situation, a model and equations.

b) How is $8 \cdot \frac{3}{4}$ related to $\frac{3}{4} \cdot 8$? Use situations, models and equations in your explanation.

**MATHEMATICALLY SPEAKING**

▶ distributive property of multiplication over addition

▶ product

# On Your Own

**Write About It**

1. **a)** Write about a situation where you would find 6 groups of $\frac{2}{3}$ and a situation where you would find $\frac{2}{3}$ of a group of 6. Write an equation for each situation. Solve it using a model of your choice.

   **b)** Explain how you might use both situations to show the commutative property of multiplication.

2. Latisha biked $2\frac{2}{3}$ miles each day for 6 days.

   **a)** How far did she bike in all? Show your answer using a model and an equation.

   **b)** Use the distributive property of multiplication over addition to explain your solution.

3. Luke's 1878 book had the following report of market prices:

   Potatoes—$\$\frac{3}{4}$ per bushel     Corn—$\$\frac{1}{2}$ per bushel

   Celery—$\$\frac{3}{4}$ per dozen     Sugar—$\$\frac{1}{20}$ per pound

   Butter—$\$\frac{3}{8}$ per pound     Baked Beans—$\$\frac{9}{10}$ per dozen cans

   Lemons—$1\frac{2}{3}$¢ each     Nails—$5\frac{1}{2}$ ¢ per pound

   **a)** In 1878, Ms. Johnson had this shopping list. Find the cost of each item. Write your answer as a fraction or mixed number in simplest terms.

   - 2 bushels of corn
   - 4 pounds of butter
   - 3 lemons
   - 2 pounds of nails

   **b)** What was the total cost of the items on Ms. Johnson's shopping list? Write your answer as a mixed number in simplest terms.

   **c)** Ms. Johnson earned $\$\frac{2}{5}$ per hour in 1878 and worked 8 hours per day. Did she earn enough in two days to pay for this order?

**d)** Use the market report and write your own problems for the following:

- $4 \cdot \frac{3}{4}$

- $3 \cdot 5\frac{1}{2}$

- Create your own problem using multiplication and the market report.

Trade problems with a partner and solve each using at least one model and at least one equation. Compare your solutions.

**4.** In 1878, Ms. Abbot made $\$\frac{3}{10}$ per hour. How many hours would she have had to work to buy a dozen cans of baked beans for $\$\frac{9}{10}$?

**5.** In 2008, Mr. Powers made $\$7\frac{1}{4}$ per hour. How many hours would he have to work to buy a dozen cans of baked beans for $\$14\frac{1}{2}$?

**6.** The following recipe makes a simple cake for 6 people. You want to make enough cake for 18 people. How much of each ingredient do you need?

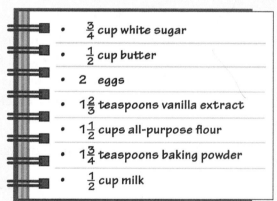

- $\frac{3}{4}$ cup white sugar
- $\frac{1}{2}$ cup butter
- 2  eggs
- $1\frac{2}{3}$ teaspoons vanilla extract
- $1\frac{1}{2}$ cups all-purpose flour
- $1\frac{3}{4}$ teaspoons baking powder
- $\frac{1}{2}$ cup milk

**7.** A necklace has 3 beads that are each $\frac{1}{2}$ inch long, 4 beads that are each $\frac{2}{3}$ inch long, and 5 beads that are each $1\frac{1}{4}$ inches long.

**a)** How long are all the beads together?

**b)** If the entire necklace is 18" long, how long is the part of the necklace with no beads?

**8.** For each of the following expressions, write a word problem that it might describe. Show each solution using at least one model. Assume that $5 \cdot \frac{4}{5}$ means 5 groups of $\frac{4}{5}$ and $\frac{4}{5} \cdot 5$ means $\frac{4}{5}$ of a group of 5.

**a)** $5 \cdot \frac{5}{6}$

**b)** $3 \cdot 3\frac{1}{2}$

**c)** $\frac{4}{5} \cdot 35$

9. Write a general rule for multiplying a whole number times a fraction. Use $6 \cdot \frac{2}{3}$ to demonstrate your rule.

10. Write a general rule for multiplying a fraction times a whole number. Use $\frac{2}{3} \cdot 6$ to demonstrate your rule. How does this compare to your rule in Question 9?

11. The seventh grade has collected the following donations for children in the hospital. They plan to donate $\frac{2}{3}$ of the items to Children's Hospital and the remaining $\frac{1}{3}$ to the Shriner's Hospital. How many of each item should be given to Children's Hospital?

   • 72 stuffed animals

   • 24 books

   • 42 puzzles

   • 18 baseball caps

   • 30 board games

12. Dylan, Kate and Paulo have a lawn-mowing business. Dylan mowed $\frac{1}{5}$ of Mr. Tully's lawn, and Kate mowed $\frac{3}{10}$ of it. Paulo mowed the rest. Paulo was paid $10 for the part he mowed. If Dylan and Kate get paid at the same rate, how much should each get? Explain your answer in pictures and equations.

13. How many 12" long drainage tiles will it take to make a drain $\frac{1}{8}$ of a mile long?

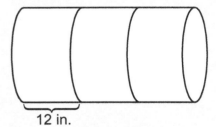

12 in.

? Hint
See page 146

14. A woman cashed her paycheck and used $\frac{3}{4}$ of it to pay her rent. She deposited the rest, $200, in her savings account. What was the total amount of her paycheck?

? Hint
See page 146

**15.** $\frac{1}{5}$ of a pole is in the mud and $\frac{2}{5}$ of the pole is in water. 14 feet of the pole is in the air. What is the total length of the pole?

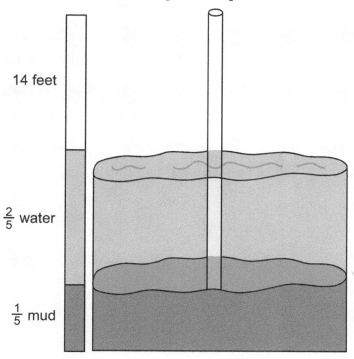

14 feet

$\frac{2}{5}$ water

$\frac{1}{5}$ mud

 Think Beyond

**16.** One-fourth of a number is 10 more than $\frac{1}{5}$ of the number. What is the number? Explain your thinking.

**? Hint**
See page 146

 Think Beyond

17. Six monkeys have a pile of bananas. After dark, the first monkey takes $\frac{1}{6}$ of the bananas and runs away. The next monkey wakes up, takes $\frac{1}{5}$ of the bananas that are left and runs away. Then, the third monkey wakes up, takes $\frac{1}{4}$ of the remaining bananas and runs away. The fourth monkey then wakes up, sees that three monkeys are gone, takes $\frac{1}{3}$ of the remaining bananas and runs away. When the fifth monkey wakes up, he sees only one monkey left. He decides to take $\frac{1}{2}$ of the bananas that are left and then he runs away. The last monkey finds all the other monkeys gone and only 5 bananas left. How many bananas were there to begin with?

**? Hint**
See page 146

 Think Beyond

18. There are 18 boys on a field trip to the museum. This is $\frac{3}{7}$ of the total number of students on the trip. How many girls are on the museum field trip? Show your work.

**Think Back**

19. **a)** What number is 1,000 more than 99,452?

    **b)** What number is 100 less than 30,049?

    **c)** What number is 10 less than 10,002?

20. Which of the following has 6 as a factor?

    **A.** 45

    **B.** 69

    **C.** 120

    **D.** 50

21. What is the value of $n$ in each of the following?

    **a)** $52 \cdot n = 5,200$

    **b)** $520 \div n = 52$

    **c)** $5,200 \div n = 52$

    **d)** $52 \cdot n = 520$

22. Find the value of $n$:

    $n = 24 + 18 \div 3 \cdot 2$

23. Write as a decimal:

    $5 + \dfrac{6}{1,000} + \dfrac{5}{10}$

# Part of a Part

→ Start It Off

Tommy uses a strategy for multiplying that he calls "doubling and halving." When multiplying two numbers, he doubles one number and takes half of the other. He then multiplies these new numbers. Study Tommy's pattern. He multiplies $4 \times 20$ two different ways.

$$4 \cdot 20 = 80 \qquad 4 \cdot 20 = 80$$
$$\cdot 2 \quad \cdot \tfrac{1}{2} \qquad \cdot \tfrac{1}{2} \quad \cdot 2$$
$$8 \cdot 10 = 80 \qquad 2 \cdot 40 = 80$$
$$\cdot \tfrac{1}{2} \quad \cdot 2$$
$$1 \cdot 80 = 80$$

1. Explain the steps that Tommy used in these examples.

$$5 \cdot 34 = 10 \cdot 17 = 170$$
$$86 \cdot 50 = 43 \cdot 100 = 4{,}300$$

Using the same pattern, fill in the blanks. Be prepared to explain your thinking.

2. $5 \cdot 22 = 10 \cdot$ _____ = _____

3. $4 \cdot 22 = 2 \cdot$ _____ = $1 \cdot$ _____ = _____

4. $48 \cdot 50 =$ _____ $\cdot 100 =$ _____

5. $246 \cdot 5 =$ _____ $\cdot$ _____ = _____

6. Talk to a partner about why Tommy's strategy works. How do you decide which number to double and which to take half of?

# Back to Nature

Luke's class thought it would be great if his school had a garden. The principal agreed to give Luke's class a plot of land behind the school for the garden. The class decided that $\frac{2}{3}$ of the garden should be used for organic vegetables. They also decided that $\frac{1}{3}$ of the garden should be used for flowers. They want $\frac{1}{4}$ of the flowers to be marigolds.

1. Talk to a partner about what part of the total garden should be marigolds. Draw an area diagram to illustrate your answer.

Ali and Devlin used a sheet of paper to represent one whole garden. They folded the paper into thirds vertically and shaded one third to represent the part of the garden that would be planted with flowers.

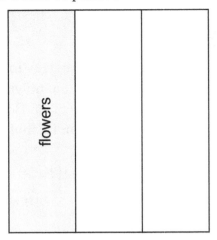

They then took the folded paper and folded this into fourths horizontally. They put an M on one of the four sections to show the part of the garden that would be marigolds.

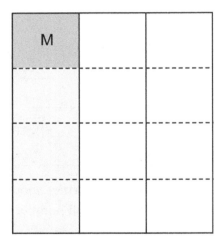

2. Look at Ali and Devlin's diagram.

   a) What fraction of the total garden will have marigolds?

   b) Does this match the part that you and your partner decided should be planted with marigolds?

   c) How is this diagram similar to a diagram you might use to show $3 \cdot 4$?

3. Mariah said that $6 \cdot \frac{2}{3}$ means to take 6 groups of $\frac{2}{3}$. She also said $\frac{2}{3} \cdot 6$ means to take $\frac{2}{3}$ of a group of 6. Mariah thinks that $\frac{1}{4} \cdot \frac{1}{3}$ must mean to take $\frac{1}{4}$ of a group of $\frac{1}{3}$. Do you agree? Use the example of the garden in your explanation.

The class decided to split the part of the garden for vegetables as follows:

- $\frac{1}{2}$ for tomatoes
- $\frac{1}{8}$ for green beans
- $\frac{3}{8}$ for carrots

For the flower part of the garden, the class decided on the following:

- $\frac{5}{8}$ for daisies
- $\frac{1}{8}$ for daylilies
- $\frac{1}{4}$ for marigolds

4. Work with a partner.

   a) Use a piece of paper to represent the whole garden. By folding or drawing, create an area diagram that shows the part of the garden that is planted with each type of vegetable or flower.

   b) What fraction of the garden is planted with each type of vegetable and flower?

   c) Add all the fractions from Part b together. What is the total? What should the total be if your fractions from Part b are correct? Why?

5. Luke's class worked hard all spring making the garden. One summer day, they harvested one whole bushel of tomatoes. They decided to give $\frac{3}{4}$ of the bushel to the local homeless shelter and $\frac{1}{4}$ of the bushel to the school's summer lunch program.

   The cooks in the summer lunch program used $\frac{2}{3}$ of the $\frac{1}{4}$ bushel of tomatoes to make spaghetti sauce. What part of one whole bushel of tomatoes did they use for the sauce? Draw a diagram or fold paper to show your solution.

6. Write a word problem for each of the following: Show how you would solve the problem using an area diagram. Be sure to show one whole on your diagram.

   a) $\frac{1}{2}$ of $\frac{3}{4}$

   b) $\frac{2}{3}$ of $\frac{3}{4}$

   c) $\frac{5}{8}$ of $\frac{2}{3}$

> **Example**
>
> When you find the total amount in 2 groups of 6, you are finding $2 \cdot 6$. When you find $\frac{2}{3}$ of 6, you are finding $\frac{2}{3} \cdot 6$. When you find $\frac{2}{3}$ of $\frac{3}{4}$, you are finding $\frac{2}{3} \cdot \frac{3}{4}$.

7. The results in Questions 5 and 6 are smaller than either fraction in the problem. When you multiply two fractions between 0 and 1, will the product always be smaller than either fraction? Try using a model or a diagram to explain your thinking.

## More Fraction Multiplication Models

8. Zoe has $\frac{2}{3}$ of a yard of string to tie tomato vines to a fence. She plans to use $\frac{1}{3}$ of the string on each of the three plants.

   a) Zoe thought if she split the thirds into thirds, she would have ninths. Explain how you might fold the string to find the amount used for each tomato plant. Mark 0, $\frac{2}{3}$ and 1 on the number line. Show how to find $\frac{1}{3}$ of $\frac{2}{3}$ using the number line.

   b) What if Zoe had $\frac{5}{6}$ of a yard of string and needed $\frac{1}{2}$ of the string? If the sixths are split in half, what fractions do you now have? Mark 0, $\frac{5}{6}$ and 1 on the number line. Show how to find $\frac{1}{2}$ of $\frac{5}{6}$ using the number line.

9. Use a number line to show the solution to each of the following:

   a) $\frac{1}{2}$ of $\frac{3}{4}$

   b) $\frac{2}{3}$ of $\frac{3}{4}$

   c) $\frac{5}{8}$ of $\frac{2}{3}$

   d) How do your solutions with the number lines compare to your solutions using area diagrams in Question 6?

   e) What patterns do you notice in the products? Give a general rule for multiplying any two fractions less than 1.

   f) How does this relate to your rule for multiplying a whole number times a fraction?

    **Hint**
   See page 146

## Wrap It Up

Willis said, "When you multiply two numbers, the product is larger than either number." When he tried this with fractions, it didn't work. Use a situation and a diagram to explain to Willis why you sometimes get a smaller number when you multiply two fractions.

**Write About It**

1. When Salli multiplies a whole number by a fraction, the product is larger than the fraction. When she multiplies a proper fraction by another proper fraction, the product is smaller than either fraction. Using a word problem and a diagram, explain to Salli why this happens.

2. Lainey bought $\frac{1}{3}$ of a pound of birdseed. She wants to put $\frac{1}{2}$ of the birdseed in each of two birdfeeders.

   a) Draw an area diagram and a number line diagram to find $\frac{1}{2}$ of $\frac{1}{3}$ of a pound of birdseed. Be sure to show one whole pound on each of your diagrams.

   b) What if Lainey bought $\frac{2}{3}$ pound of birdseed? Draw two diagrams to show how you would find $\frac{1}{2}$ of $\frac{2}{3}$.

   c) How are these problems related to multiplying whole numbers?

3. Luke and Gino picked a pound of green beans. They each took half of the beans home to their families. Gino's father used $\frac{2}{3}$ of Gino's beans for their dinner. What part of a pound of beans did Gino's father use?

4. The relay team has four members. Each member swims $\frac{1}{4}$ of the race. If the race is $\frac{2}{3}$ of a mile, how far does each team member swim?

5. In another garden, $\frac{3}{4}$ of the garden was planted with flowers. Of the flowers, $\frac{2}{3}$ were violets. Explain how to use this diagram to find the part of the garden that was planted with violets.

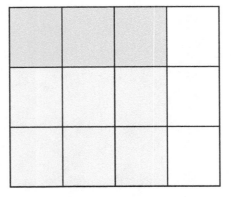

6. $\frac{3}{5}$ of the students in a class are girls. $\frac{2}{3}$ of the girls in the class have brown hair. What part of the whole class are girls with brown hair?

7. Complete the following multiplication table. Write your answers in simplest form.

| × | $\frac{1}{2}$ | $\frac{1}{3}$ | $\frac{3}{4}$ |
|---|---|---|---|
| $\frac{3}{5}$ | | | |
| $\frac{2}{3}$ | | | |
| $\frac{7}{6}$ | | | |

8. In three days, Meredith swam $\frac{2}{3}$ of a mile. If she swam the same distance each day, how far did she swim in two days? Use a number line and an equation to show your answer.

9. Lynley said that $\frac{1}{2}$ of $\frac{1}{8}$ is $\frac{1}{4}$ because $\frac{1}{2}$ of 8 is 4. Was he right? Draw a diagram to illustrate your answer.

10. Write a word problem for each of the following: Draw a diagram using an area model or a number line. Write an equation to show each of your solutions.

   a) $\frac{5}{8} \cdot \frac{2}{3}$

   b) $\frac{4}{5} \cdot \frac{1}{2}$

   c) $\frac{3}{4} \cdot \frac{2}{6}$

11. It took Riley 1 hour and 45 minutes to drive from Lexington to Cincinnati. He left Lexington at 10:30 am. What time did he arrive in Cincinnati?

12. Jackson has $40. Ciera has $10 less than Jackson. Ciera has twice as much money as Jody. How much money do all three have together?

13. These two rectangles have the same area.

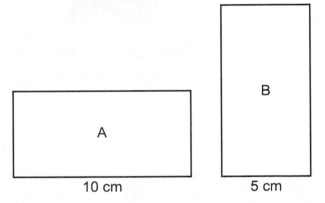

Rectangle A has a perimeter of 32 cm. What is the perimeter of rectangle B?

14. Solve for $n$.

$$32.508 = 32 + \frac{5}{10} + \frac{8}{n}$$

15. Fill in the blanks:

a) 5 liters = _____ milliliters

b) 15 meters = _____ centimeters

c) 6 yards = _____ inches

d) 3 miles = _____ feet

# LESSON 1.3 Are Fraction Algorithms Rational?

➡️ **Start It Off**

Bharat wondered if Tommy's doubling and halving strategy would work for fractions. He knew that he could double $\frac{1}{2}$ and get 1. He then decided he should take half of the other factor. He tried the following:

$$\frac{1}{2} \cdot 14 = 1 \cdot 7 = 7$$

$$\frac{1}{4} \cdot 24 = \frac{1}{2} \cdot 12 = 1 \cdot 6 = 6$$

Use doubling and halving on the following:

1. $\frac{1}{2} \cdot 22 = 1 \cdot \underline{\hspace{1cm}} = \underline{\hspace{1cm}}$

2. $\frac{1}{4} \cdot 28 = \frac{1}{2} \cdot \underline{\hspace{1cm}} = 1 \cdot \underline{\hspace{1cm}} = \underline{\hspace{1cm}}$

3. $\frac{1}{8} \cdot 48 = \frac{1}{4} \cdot 24 = $

4. $\frac{1}{2} \cdot 64$

5. $\frac{1}{4} \cdot 32$

6. Make up another doubling and halving problem using $\frac{1}{2}$ or $\frac{1}{4}$ and a whole number. Does the strategy work? Be prepared to explain your reasoning.

# Developing Algorithms for Multiplying Fractions

When multiplying, you don't always want to have to draw diagrams or fold paper. Sometimes, you just want to use numbers or words for the solution. You have developed some algorithms for solving multiplication problems with fractions. In this lesson, you will explore these rules further.

1. In the last lesson, you developed a rule for multiplying whole numbers and fractions in any order. Demonstrate your rule on the following:

   a) $\frac{3}{4} \cdot 20$

   b) $\frac{2}{5} \cdot 15$

   c) $8 \cdot \frac{3}{5}$

   d) $4 \cdot \frac{2}{3}$

2. Matt said that when he multiplies a fraction by a whole number, he first multiplies the numerator by the whole number. He then divides the answer by the denominator. Jerra says that she does the opposite. She first divides the whole number by the denominator. She then multiplies the answer by the numerator. For example, to multiply $\frac{2}{3} \cdot 6$, Matt first multiplies $2 \cdot 6$ to get 12. He then divides 12 by 3 to get 4. Jerra first divides 6 by 3 to get 2. She then multiplies $2 \cdot 2$ to get 4.

   a) Try both methods for the problems in Question 1. Do both methods work?

   b) Which method do you prefer? Does it depend on the problem?

3. Mona said that she writes the whole number as a fraction with a denominator of 1. She then multiplies the numerators together and multiplies the denominators together.

   a) Try Mona's method on the problems in Question 1. Does this give the same answer as the other methods?

   b) Which method do you prefer? Does it depend on the problem?

4. Choose one method and fill out the multiplication table. Talk to a partner about the method that you use.

| × | 24 | 20 | 36 |
|---|---|---|---|
| $\frac{2}{5}$ | | | |
| $\frac{2}{3}$ | | | |
| $\frac{7}{6}$ | | | |

In the last lesson, you also multiplied two proper fractions.

5. Talk to a partner about an algorithm to multiply two fractions between 0 and 1.

   a) Make up three expressions involving multiplying two fractions. Use your algorithm to find the products.

   b) Draw a diagram to illustrate each of your three expressions. Do your diagrams support your algorithm? Explain.

Do you remember the identity for multiplication? The identity for multiplication is 1. When you multiply any number by 1, you get that number. In symbols, for any number $a$, $a \cdot 1 = 1 \cdot a = a$.

**6.** Use your algorithm for multiplying a whole number by a fraction or mixed number for the following:

a) $\frac{3}{4} \cdot 1$

b) $1 \cdot \frac{5}{6}$

c) $2\frac{4}{5} \cdot 1$

d) How does using your algorithm relate to what you know about the identity for multiplication?

**7.** What happens when you multiply a fraction or mixed number by a number that is equivalent to 1? Use your algorithm for multiplying two fractions or mixed numbers for the following:

a) $\frac{4}{7} \cdot \frac{5}{5}$

b) $\frac{4}{4} \cdot \frac{2}{5}$

c) $2\frac{1}{3} \cdot \frac{2}{2}$

d) $\frac{3}{3} \cdot 3\frac{1}{2}$

e) Simplify each product in Parts a through d. What pattern do you notice?

f) Explain how multiplying by a fraction equivalent to 1 can help you find equivalent fractions.

**8.** Use your algorithm for multiplying fractions to find each of the following: What pattern do you notice?

a) $\frac{5}{8} \cdot \frac{8}{5}$      d) $3 \cdot \frac{1}{3}$

b) $\frac{3}{4} \cdot \frac{4}{3}$      e) $\frac{1}{4} \cdot 4$

c) $\frac{3}{2} \cdot \frac{2}{3}$      f) $2\frac{1}{2} \cdot \frac{5}{2}$

Two numbers whose product is 1 are called reciprocals. A reciprocal of a number is called its multiplicative inverse. When you multiply a number by its inverse, the product is 1, the identity for multiplication.

9. What is the reciprocal of each of the following? Show that the product of each of these numbers and its reciprocal is equal to 1.

a) $\frac{3}{7}$

b) $\frac{4}{9}$

c) $\frac{1}{4}$

d) 4

e) $\frac{8}{5}$

f) $1\frac{3}{5}$

g) Explain how you would find the reciprocal of any whole number, fraction or mixed number. Use an example to show your method.

## Simplify First?

It is sometimes easier to simplify before multiplying fractions. To find $\frac{2}{3} \cdot 18$, you could multiply $18 \cdot 2$ to get 36. You can then divide by 3 to get 12. But it might be quicker to first divide 18 by 3 to get 6. You can then multiply by 2 to get an answer of 12.

Luke's book from 1878 used this idea. It showed how to "cancel" factors before multiplying fractions. Each of the numbers in the fractions was first written as the product of prime factors. For example, $\frac{6}{10} \cdot \frac{2}{9}$ was rewritten as $\frac{2 \cdot 3}{2 \cdot 5} \cdot \frac{2}{3 \cdot 3}$. Canceling was used to divide the same factors from the numerator and the denominator. In this example, one of the 3s and one of the 2s was divided from both the numerators and the denominators.

$$\frac{2 \cdot 3}{2 \cdot 5} \cdot \frac{2}{3 \cdot 3} = \frac{\cancel{2} \cdot \cancel{3}}{\cancel{2} \cdot 5} \cdot \frac{2}{\cancel{3} \cdot 3} = \frac{2}{5 \cdot 3} = \frac{2}{15}$$

Canceling is often a good way to simplify multiplication of fractions.

Let's use canceling for $\frac{8}{9} \cdot \frac{3}{4}$.

- First, write the prime factorizations of 8, 9 and 4.

$$8 = 2 \cdot 2 \cdot 2$$

$$9 = 3 \cdot 3$$

$$4 = 2 \cdot 2$$

- Next, rewrite the fractions using the prime factors.

$$\frac{8}{9} \cdot \frac{3}{4} = \frac{2 \cdot 2 \cdot 2}{3 \cdot 3} \cdot \frac{3}{2 \cdot 2}$$

- Then, cancel matching factors in the numerator and denominator.

$$\frac{8}{9} \cdot \frac{3}{4} = \frac{\cancel{2} \cdot \cancel{2} \cdot 2}{\cancel{3} \cdot 3} \cdot \frac{\cancel{3}}{\cancel{2} \cdot \cancel{2}}$$

- Multiply the remaining numbers.

$$\frac{1 \cdot 1 \cdot 2 \cdot 1}{1 \cdot 3 \cdot 1 \cdot 1} = \frac{2}{3}$$

10. For Parts a and b, write the prime factorizations of the numerators and denominators. Then cancel the common factors before finding the products.

a) $\frac{5}{12} \cdot \frac{3}{10}$

b) $\frac{4}{15} \cdot \frac{6}{20}$

c) Multiply the fractions in Parts a and b without canceling and simplify each product. Compare your answers.

11. Juanita said she could cancel without first finding prime factors. She said you could multiply $\frac{4}{15} \cdot \frac{6}{20}$ by first dividing the 4 and the 20 each by 4. She said you could then divide the 6 and the 15 each by 3. The problem then becomes $\frac{\cancel{4}^{1}}{\cancel{15}^{5}} \cdot \frac{\cancel{6}^{2}}{\cancel{20}^{5}} = \frac{1}{5} \cdot \frac{2}{5} = \frac{2}{25}$.

a) Compare this to your answer to Question 10b. Do both of these methods give the same answer?

b) How are the equations $\frac{6}{7} \cdot \frac{2}{3} = \frac{12}{21}$ and $\frac{2}{7} \cdot \frac{2}{1} = \frac{4}{7}$ the same? How do you know?

c) Show how you might use canceling for each of the following expressions.

$\frac{6}{21} \cdot \frac{7}{8}$

$\frac{4}{5} \cdot \frac{10}{11}$

$\frac{4}{9} \cdot \frac{12}{18}$

**d)** For each of the expressions in Part c, find the products without canceling first. Simplify your answers. Did you get the same product?

**e)** Which method do you prefer? Does the method affect your answer?

**12.** Lora said that you should divide each of the 2s by 2 before multiplying $\frac{2}{7} \cdot \frac{2}{1}$. Does Lora's method work? Explain.

# Wrap It Up


Talk to a partner about each of the following questions:

- What algorithm could you use to multiply a whole number by a fraction?

- What algorithm could you use to multiply two proper fractions?

- How do these algorithms compare?

- Do you prefer canceling before multiplying or do you simplify your answer after multiplying without canceling? Does your method affect the final product?

> **MATHEMATICALLY SPEAKING**
> - identity for multiplication (multiplicative identity)
> - multiplicative inverse
> - reciprocal

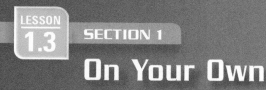

**Write About It**

1. Can the same rule you use for multiplying a fraction by a whole number be used for multiplying two fractions? Explain.

2. Complete the table using any method. Show your work.

| × | 32 | 18 | $\frac{4}{5}$ | $\frac{2}{3}$ |
|---|----|----|----|----|
| 3 | | | | |
| $\frac{3}{4}$ | | | | |
| $\frac{2}{9}$ | | | | |
| $\frac{3}{2}$ | | | | |

3. Look at Lynnette's answers to the following:

$$\frac{1}{4} \cdot 5 = \frac{5}{20}$$

$$\frac{2}{3} \cdot 4 = \frac{8}{12}$$

$$\frac{3}{4} \cdot 3 = \frac{9}{12}$$

a) How do you think Lynette found the product for each of these?

b) Does Lynette's method work? How would you help Lynette correct her mistake?

4. Find the reciprocal:

a) $\frac{3}{4}$

b) 5

c) $2\frac{2}{9}$

d) Multiply each number in Parts a, b and c by its reciprocal. What is the product?

5. For parts a, b, and c, tell whether the numbers are multiplicative inverses.

a) $\frac{2}{9}$ and $\frac{9}{2}$

b) $2\frac{2}{3}$ and $2\frac{3}{2}$

c) $\frac{4}{2}$ and $\frac{2}{1}$

d) For each pair of numbers that are not multiplicative inverses, give the reciprocal of the first number. Write the reciprocal in simplest form.

6. For Parts a, b and c, find the prime factorization of each numerator and denominator and cancel before multiplying. Show your work.

   a) $\frac{8}{15} \cdot \frac{5}{12}$

   b) $\frac{5}{9} \cdot \frac{3}{8}$

   c) $\frac{8}{25} \cdot \frac{10}{24}$

   d) For each of the problems in Parts a, b and c, multiply first and then simplify the answer. Did you get the same answers?

7. For Parts a, b and c, cancel first without factoring and then multiply.

   a) $\frac{3}{7} \cdot \frac{5}{12}$

   b) $\frac{2}{9} \cdot \frac{3}{8}$

   c) $\frac{4}{5} \cdot \frac{10}{12}$

   d) For each of the problems in Parts a, b and c, multiply first and then simplify the answer. Did you get the same answers?

   e) Do you prefer canceling first and then multiplying or multiplying first and then simplifying the product? Explain.

8. Jeremiah used a copier to reduce a picture to $\frac{3}{4}$ of its original size. What fraction would he have to enlarge his copy by to get another copy that is the same size as the original?

9. Lara said that sometimes switching the numerators of the fractions she is multiplying makes the problem easier. For example, she changes $\frac{3}{4} \cdot \frac{2}{6}$ to $\frac{2}{4} \cdot \frac{3}{6}$. She knows this is the same as $\frac{1}{2} \cdot \frac{1}{2}$, which is $\frac{1}{4}$.

   a) Try Lara's method.

   $\frac{4}{6} \cdot \frac{3}{16}$

   $\frac{6}{8} \cdot \frac{4}{12}$

   $\frac{6}{18} \cdot \frac{9}{24}$

   b) Does Lara's method always work? Explain.

   c) How does this compare to canceling?

**Think Beyond**

10. Does zero have a reciprocal? Explain.

11. Fill in the blanks:

$$
\begin{array}{r}
5\_ \\
\times\ \_2 \\
\hline
12 \\
100 \\
4\_0 \\
\_000 \\
\hline
\_5\_2
\end{array}
$$

12. Estimate the sum to the nearest whole number.

   a) $\frac{2}{3} + \frac{8}{9}$    b) $18\frac{1}{4} - 12\frac{1}{3}$    c) $5\frac{2}{9} + 6\frac{4}{5}$

13. Find the following: Do not use a calculator. Show your work.

   a) $56\overline{)2,376}$    b) $45\overline{)943}$    c) $856 \cdot 79$

14. Which of the following does NOT appear to be a parallelogram?

   A.

   B.

   C.

   D.

   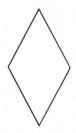

15. Copy the following rectangle and sketch all lines of symmetry.

# Multiplying Mixed Numbers

## ➡️ Start It Off

Finding the area of a rectangle is one way to model multiplication. For example, this diagram can be used to model 13 · 11. Notice that the 13-by-11 rectangle can be broken into four smaller rectangles.

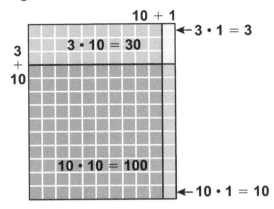

1. How are the four small rectangles related to the partial products in 13 · 11? Note that in the multiplication problem below the four partial products are 3, 30, 10 and 100. How do the rectangles relate to finding $(10 + 3) \cdot (10 + 1)$ using the distributive property of multiplication over addition?

$$
\begin{array}{r}
11 \\
\times\ 13 \\
\hline
3 \\
30 \\
10 \\
100 \\
\hline
143
\end{array}
$$

2. The diagram below is a model for 14 · 15. Find the area of the four smaller rectangles.

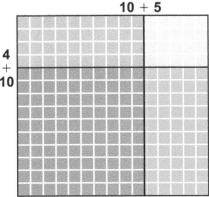

3. Find the product of 14 · 15 using four partial products. Match each partial product to one of the smaller rectangles in the diagram in Question 2. How is the diagram related to finding (10 + 4) · (10 + 5) using the distributive property of multiplication over addition?

4. How might you use this diagram to find the product of 23 · 38?

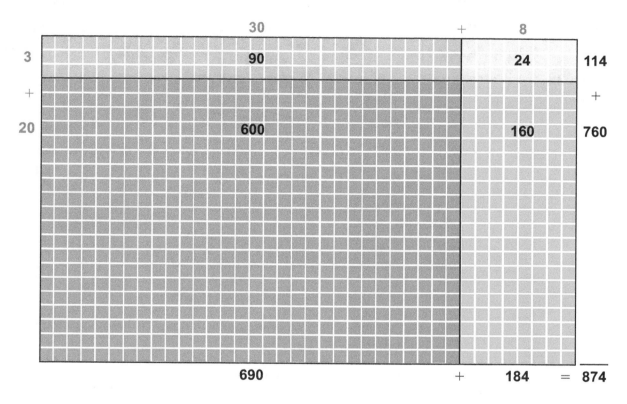

# The Vegetable Stand

Luke's class decided to sell the vegetables they grew in the garden. They liked writing money amounts as fractions. They decided on the following prices.

**SALE PRICE**

| | |
|---|---|
| Tomatoes | $2\frac{2}{5}$ per pound |
| Carrots | $1\frac{1}{4}$ per pound |
| Green beans | $1\frac{3}{4}$ per pound |

1. Ms. Lopez wants to buy $1\frac{1}{2}$ pounds of tomatoes.

   a) Estimate how much the tomatoes will cost. Will they cost more than $3? Will $5 be enough?

   b) Talk to a partner about how you might find the exact cost.

   c) Luke said that 1 pound would cost $2\frac{2}{5}$. Another $\frac{1}{2}$ pound would cost half of that. Half of $2 is $1 and half of 2 fifths is 1 fifth. So, $\frac{1}{2}$ pound of tomatoes would cost $1 + \$\frac{1}{5}$. Use Luke's method to find the cost of $1\frac{1}{2}$ pounds of tomatoes. Does this match the amount you and your partner calculated?

   d) $1\frac{1}{2}$ is the same as $1 + \frac{1}{2}$. How might you use the distributive property of multiplication over addition to find $(1 + \frac{1}{2}) \cdot (2 + \frac{2}{5})$? How does this compare to Luke's method in Part c?

   e) Ms. Lopez said that you could change both $1\frac{1}{2}$ and $2\frac{2}{5}$ to improper fractions. $1\frac{1}{2} = \frac{3}{2}$ and $2\frac{2}{5} = \frac{12}{5}$. She said you could then multiply the numerators and denominators like any other fractions. What is $\frac{3}{2} \cdot \frac{12}{5}$? Write your answer as a mixed number in simplest form. Does this give the same answer?

   f) Steph changed the fractions to decimals. She knows $\$2\frac{2}{5} = \$2.40$. So 1 pound would cost $2.40 and half a pound would cost half of that. Would Steph get the same answer?

**2.** How much should the class charge for each of the following? Estimate your answer first. Then use one method to find the cost and a second method to check your answer. Make a chart like this and show your work.

| Amount | Estimate | First Method | Second Method |
|---|---|---|---|
| **a)** $2\frac{2}{5}$ pounds of carrots | | | |
| **b)** $3\frac{3}{5}$ pounds of green beans | | | |
| **c)** $4\frac{3}{10}$ pounds of tomatoes | | | |

**3.** Make up your own problems about purchases at the vegetable stand. Trade with a partner and solve each other's problems. Do your solutions agree? Did you use the same methods?

## Garden Plots

Each student in Luke's class wanted his or her own garden plot.

**4.** Clara's plot is $1\frac{2}{3}$ yards by $1\frac{1}{3}$ yards. Clara knows that this is more than 1 square yard, but she is not sure how much more.

    **a)** Estimate whether Clara's plot is at least 2 square yards. Is it at least 4 square yards?

Clara drew the following diagram to help figure this out.

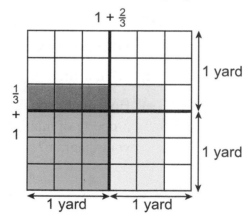

    **b)** Talk to a partner about how to find the area of Clara's plot. Where is 1 square yard on the diagram?

**c)** What part of 1 square yard is each of the small squares? How many small squares are in Clara's plot? What is the total area of Clara's plot? Does this match your estimate?

**d)** Dan said that you could multiply $1 \cdot 1$ and add $\frac{2}{3} \cdot \frac{1}{3}$ to find the area of Clara's plot. Would this work? Explain.

**e)** Using the distributive property of multiplication over addition, you can write:
$$\left(1 + \tfrac{1}{3}\right) \cdot \left(1 + \tfrac{2}{3}\right) = (1 \cdot 1) + \left(\tfrac{1}{3} \cdot 1\right) + \left(\tfrac{2}{3} \cdot 1\right) + \left(\tfrac{1}{3} \cdot \tfrac{2}{3}\right)$$
How does this equation show the area of each rectangle? What is the total area?

**f)** $1\frac{2}{3}$ can be written as $\frac{5}{3}$ and $1\frac{1}{3}$ can be written as $\frac{4}{3}$. How might you find the product of $\frac{5}{3} \cdot \frac{4}{3}$? How does this match the diagram?

**5.** Monique had a plot that is $1\frac{2}{3}$ yards by $1\frac{2}{4}$ yards. She drew this diagram to show her plot.

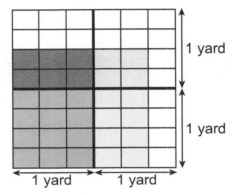

**a)** Write the length and width of the rectangle as improper fractions.

**b)** Where on the diagram is 1 square yard?

**c)** What is the area of each of the small rectangles in the diagram?

**d)** What is the area of Monique's plot?

**e)** How might you find the area of the plot using the distributive property of multiplication over addition? How does this relate to your diagram?

6. What are the length, width and area of each of the following? Locate 1 square yard in each diagram, label the length and width, and write an equation for the area of each of the four sections and for total area.

   **a)** Casey's Plot

   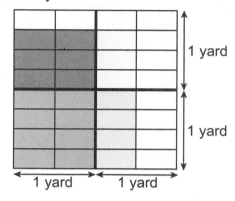

   **b.** Jessica's Plot

   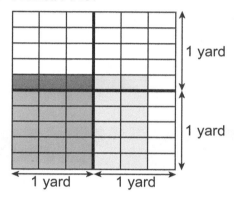

   **c)** Who had the larger plot?

7. For each of the garden plots on the chart, estimate the area of the plot. Then find the area using any algorithm. Show your work.

| Dimensions | Estimate of Area | Exact Area |
|---|---|---|
| $\frac{1}{4}$ yard by $\frac{3}{5}$ yard | | |
| $5\frac{2}{5}$ yards by $6\frac{2}{3}$ yards | | |
| $\frac{1}{2}$ yard by $7\frac{3}{4}$ yards | | |

8. Talk to a partner about whether each of the following statements is always, sometimes or never true. Give an example to support each answer. Be prepared to share your reasoning and examples with the class.

| Statement | Always, Sometimes or Never True? | Example |
|---|---|---|
| **a)** If two numbers are each greater than 1, their product will be greater than both numbers. | | |
| **b)** If one number is greater than 1 and one number is less than 1 but greater than 0, the product will be less than both of the numbers. | | |
| **c)** If two positive numbers are each less than 1, their product will be greater than 1. | | |

 **W rap It Up**

How can you tell in advance whether the product of two fractions or mixed numbers will be larger than either of the two numbers? Use word problems and diagrams in your explanation.

# LESSON 1.4    SECTION 1
# On Your Own

 **Write About It**

1. Bill said that when he multiplies two fractions between 0 and 1, the product is always less than 1, but when he multiplies two improper fractions, the product is always greater than 1. Is Bill right? Explain using a word problem and a diagram.

2. You would like to buy $5\frac{3}{5}$ pounds of cheese. Cheese costs $3\frac{1}{4}$ per pound.

   a) Estimate whether the cost is more or less than $20.00.

   b) Find the exact cost. Show your work.

3. A rectangular painting is $2\frac{3}{4}$ feet by $3\frac{2}{3}$ feet. What is the area of the painting? Draw an area diagram to show your solution.

4. Find one fraction, one mixed number and one whole number so that each has a product greater than $\frac{3}{7}$ when it is multiplied by $\frac{3}{7}$.

5. Write a word problem and an equation for the following diagram. Be sure to include the answer.

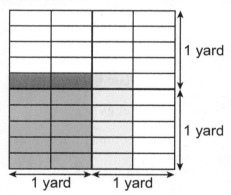

6. For each of the following, decide if the statement is always, sometimes or never true. Give an example to support each answer. If it is sometimes true, give one example to show when it is true and one example to show when it is false.

| Statement | Always, Sometimes or Never True? | Example |
|---|---|---|
| a) If two numbers are each greater than 1, their product will be greater than 1. | | |
| b) If one number is greater than 1 and one number is less than 1, their product will be equal to 1. | | |
| c) If two positive numbers are each less than 1, their product will be less than either number. | | |

7. The following cookie recipe will make 50 oatmeal raisin cookies. List the ingredients you would need for 125 cookies.

- $\frac{3}{4}$ cup butter
- 2 eggs
- $2\frac{1}{3}$ cups flour
- $1\frac{1}{4}$ cups oatmeal
- $1\frac{1}{4}$ cups sugar
- 1 teaspoon baking soda
- $\frac{1}{2}$ teaspoon salt
- $\frac{2}{3}$ cup nuts
- 1 cup raisins
- 1 teaspoon cinnamon
- 2 teaspoons vanilla

8. Fewer than half of 13- and 17-year-old students who took a test could answer the following questions. What should they have answered for each?

   **a)** What is $3\frac{1}{2} \cdot 6\frac{2}{3}$?

   **b)** A recipe for punch calls for $3\frac{3}{4}$ cups of pineapple juice to serve 10 people. How much pineapple juice should be used to make the same punch recipe to serve 5 people?

9. Complete this multiplication chart.

   | × | $1\frac{1}{2}$ | $2\frac{3}{4}$ |
   |---|---|---|
   | $\frac{3}{5}$ | | |
   | $2\frac{2}{3}$ | | |

10. Jess said that if she takes $\frac{1}{4}$ of $1\frac{3}{4}$, she gets $1\frac{1}{2}$. Is she correct? Explain.

11. Ali says that $2\frac{1}{2} \cdot 1\frac{3}{4} = (2 \cdot 1) + \left(\frac{1}{2} \cdot \frac{3}{4}\right)$. Is he right? Use a diagram to explain.

12. The radius of a circle is $2\frac{4}{5}$ feet. What is the diameter?

13. What is the approximate area of this figure?

14. When you start a movie, the clock on the wall looks like this:

    The movie will end in 1 hour and 45 minutes. What time will it be at the end of the movie?

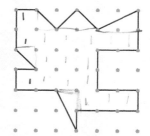

15. The graph shows the favorite fruits of the students in Mr. Hannah's class.

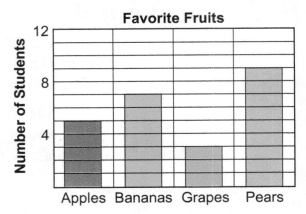

**Favorite Fruits**

a) What part of the class said grapes are their favorite fruit? Give your answer as a fraction, a decimal and a percent.

b) What part of the class said either apples or bananas are their favorite fruits? Give your answer as a fraction, a decimal and a percent.

16. For lunch at the Highlands Middle School, students can order white milk, chocolate milk, lemonade or water. Drinks come in sizes small, medium and large. List all the possible drinks that a student might order.

# LESSON 1.5 Rational Calculating

 For most of this section, you did not use a calculator as you thought about multiplying fractions. For this lesson, though, you may use a calculator.

## ➡ Start It Off

Use your calculator to find the following products. Simplify your answers.

1. $\frac{3}{4} \cdot \frac{4}{3}$

2. $\frac{5}{8} \cdot \frac{8}{5}$

3. $\frac{2}{3} \cdot 1\frac{1}{2}$

Without using a calculator, write the fraction that you should multiply each number by in Questions 4–6 to get the same product as in Questions 1–3. Explain your thinking. Check your answer with a calculator.

4. $3\frac{2}{3}$

5. $4\frac{1}{2}$

6. $2\frac{3}{5}$

## Target Games

In the **Target Practice** game, you will work with a partner to sharpen your estimation and multiplication skills. You will be asked to find the value of $n$ in problems like $\frac{2}{3} \cdot n = 2\frac{1}{3}$. One way to do this is to guess a number and then check the product. Try $n = 3$ to get $\frac{2}{3} \cdot 3 = \frac{6}{3} = 2$. The product is too small. You need to try a larger value for $n$. Since $\frac{1}{3}$ is half of $\frac{2}{3}$, try $\frac{2}{3} \cdot 3\frac{1}{2}$. The product is $\frac{2}{3} \cdot 3\frac{1}{2} = 2\frac{1}{3}$

## · · · · · Target Practice · · · · ·

**Players:** Two teams of 2 players each

**Materials:** One set of Target Practice cards, one record sheet for each team, calculator with fraction capabilities

**Goal:** To find the fractions or mixed numbers to solve the most equations

**DIRECTIONS:**

1. Team A draws a card from the Target Practice card pile. Partners agree on a good choice for *n*, using only mental math. Team A records their guess and uses a calculator to check. Only multiplication may be used on the calculator. Team A simplifies the product on the calculator, shows it to Team B, and records it. If Team A's guess is correct, they score 1 point for the round.

2. If Team A is incorrect, Team B records a new guess for *n* for the same problem. Team B should use the information from Team A's product to refine their guess. If Team B is correct, they score 1 point for the round. If not, play continues on the same equation until one team solves for *n* or until each team has had three guesses.

3. After one team solves the first equation or both teams have had three guesses, Team B draws a new card and attempts to solve it. Each team gets one guess per turn until one team solves the equation or both teams have had three guesses. A round is over after both teams pick a Target Card from the Target Practice card pile.

4. The team with the highest score after 10 rounds is the winner.

After playing the Target Practice game, Mr. Sampson's class discussed their strategies for the equation $1\frac{3}{4} \cdot n = 2\frac{11}{12}$. Troy said that *n* had to be greater than 1 but less than 2. He guessed $1\frac{1}{2}$ and put $1\frac{3}{4} \cdot 1\frac{1}{2}$ in his calculator. The product was $2\frac{5}{8}$.

1. Should the next guess be larger or smaller than $1\frac{1}{2}$? Explain.

2. What might the denominator of the new guess be? Why?

3. Record a new guess and use multiplication on your calculator to check. Were you right? If not, keep guessing and record the equation for each guess until you solve for *n*. Discuss your thinking with a partner.

4. Make up a new multiplication equation with one of the factors missing. Trade problems with a partner. Discuss your thinking.

 **Wrap It Up**

When you multiply two positive numbers, the product is less than either of the numbers. What do you know about the two numbers? Explain.

**Write About It**

1. $\frac{3}{4}$ is multiplied by a fraction. The product is greater than 1. What do you know about the size of the other fraction? Explain.

2. Use mental math:

   a) $1\frac{3}{4} \cdot 4$

   b) $1\frac{3}{4} \cdot \frac{1}{2}$

   c) $1\frac{3}{4} \cdot 4\frac{1}{2}$

   d) How does the distributive property of multiplication over addition help you find the answer in Part c?

3. First, guess a value of $n$ to make each of the following statements true. Then find the value of $n$. You may use your calculator.

   a) $\frac{2}{3} \cdot n = 5\frac{13}{15}$

   b) $11\frac{3}{8} = 1\frac{3}{4} \cdot n$

   c) $1\frac{1}{2} \cdot n = 7\frac{1}{8}$

   d) Choose one of these problems and explain your strategy. What numbers did you guess before solving it?

4. In the **Target Practice** game, Jackson is trying to find $n$ in $1\frac{1}{2} \cdot n = 6\frac{3}{4}$. His first guess is 4. Jackson multiplies and finds $1\frac{1}{2} \cdot 4 = 6$. What should Jackson guess next? Explain.

5. Try these problems from Luke's book. You may do these by hand as they did in 1878, or use your calculator. Write the equations you use to solve each problem.

   a) If 9 tons of hay are worth $100\frac{4}{5}$, what must I give for 14 tons?

   b) How much must I pay for $18\frac{1}{2}$ cords of wood at the rate of $6\frac{2}{3}$ for 3 cords?

   c) If a man can earn $5\frac{1}{4}$ in 3 days, how much can he earn in 5 days?

   d) If a seamstress earns $1\frac{1}{3}$ in two days, how much will she earn in $10\frac{1}{2}$ days?

Write and solve equations and show your work for each of the following: Use a calculator if you wish.

6. Mr. Jackson needs exactly $3\frac{3}{4}$ pounds of nuts. He can choose up to three packages of each of the following types of nuts. What should he buy?

   Peanuts: $\frac{1}{2}$ pound      Cashews: $\frac{7}{8}$ pound      Pecans: $\frac{1}{3}$ pound

7. Jake took half of the cherries in the bowl. Jen took $\frac{1}{3}$ of the cherries. Together they took 25 cherries. How many cherries were in the bowl originally?

 **Hint**
See page 146

8. Aisha has twice as much cheese as Meredith. Meredith has three times as much cheese as Jeremy. Together the three of them have $6\frac{2}{3}$ pounds of cheese. How much cheese does Meredith have?

 **Hint**
See page 146

 **Think Beyond**

9. Sometimes the sum of a pair of numbers can equal the product of the same pair.

$$2 + 2 = 4 \qquad\qquad 2 \cdot 2 = 4$$
$$3 + 1\frac{1}{2} = 4\frac{1}{2} \qquad\qquad 3 \cdot 1\frac{1}{2} = 4\frac{1}{2}$$
$$10 + 1\frac{1}{9} = 11\frac{1}{9} \qquad\qquad 10 \cdot 1\frac{1}{9} = 11\frac{1}{9}$$

Find three other pairs of numbers whose sum is equal to their product.

 **Think Beyond**

10. Use each of the digits 1, 2, 3, 4, 5, 6, 7, 8, 9 once to make these equations true.

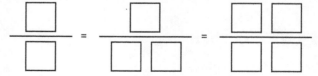

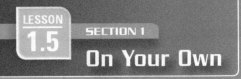
 **Think Back**

11. Is the sum of three consecutive numbers odd or even? Explain.

12. Without using a calculator, arrange the following fractions in order from the least to the greatest:

$$\frac{3}{8}, \frac{3}{2}, \frac{4}{5}, \frac{6}{7}, \frac{5}{4}$$

13. Melanie, Herb, Keisha and Bart are standing in line. List all the different orders that they could be in. For example, one possibility is MHKB—Melanie first, then Herb, then Keisha and finally Bart.

14. Arrange the figures in order from the least to the greatest area. Show your work.

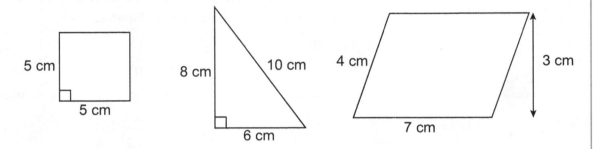

15. Arrange the figures in Question 14 in order from the least to the greatest perimeter. Show your work.

 **Optional Technology Lesson for this section available in your eBook**

# Sum It Up

In this section, you extended your understanding of multiplication of fractions as you explored multiplying whole numbers, proper and improper fractions and mixed numbers.

## Multiplication with Fractions

- When you multiply a whole number by a fraction, you can show this as repeated addition. For example, $3 \cdot \frac{3}{4} = \frac{3}{4} + \frac{3}{4} + \frac{3}{4} = \frac{9}{4}$. This has the same effect as multiplying the numerator of the fraction by the whole number: $3 \cdot \frac{3}{4} = \frac{3 \cdot 3}{4} = \frac{9}{4}$. Note that you could also write this as $3 \cdot \frac{3}{4} = \frac{3}{1} \cdot \frac{3}{4} = \frac{3 \cdot 3}{1 \cdot 4} = \frac{9}{4}$.

- You use multiplication to find the total of a number of equal groups or portion of one group. For example, 3 groups of 8 is written as $3 \cdot 8$. Similarly, $\frac{3}{4}$ of a group of 8 is written as $\frac{3}{4} \cdot 8$. If you have $\frac{3}{4}$ of $\frac{2}{3}$, this can be written as $\frac{3}{4} \cdot \frac{2}{3}$.

- When multiplying two fractions, $\frac{a}{b}$ and $\frac{c}{d}$, you can multiply the numerators and denominators to find the product, $\frac{a}{b} \cdot \frac{c}{d} = \frac{a \cdot c}{b \cdot d}$. For example, $\frac{3}{4} \cdot \frac{5}{7} = \frac{3 \cdot 5}{4 \cdot 7} = \frac{15}{28}$.

- To multiply mixed numbers, you can first change the mixed numbers to improper fractions and then multiply. For example, $3\frac{3}{4} \cdot 1\frac{1}{2} = \frac{15}{4} \cdot \frac{3}{2} = \frac{15 \cdot 3}{4 \cdot 2} = \frac{45}{8} = 5\frac{5}{8}$.

## Properties of Fraction Multiplication

■ Multiplication of fractions is commutative: $a \cdot b = b \cdot a$. For example, $\frac{3}{4} \cdot 8 = 8 \cdot \frac{3}{4}$.

■ Multiplication of fractions is distributive over addition: $a \cdot (b + c) = ab + ac$. For example,
$$\frac{3}{4} \cdot 8\frac{1}{2} = \frac{3}{4} \cdot \left(8 + \frac{1}{2}\right) = \left(\frac{3}{4} \cdot 8\right) + \left(\frac{3}{4} \cdot \frac{1}{2}\right)$$

■ You can find equivalent fractions by multiplying the original fraction by some form of the multiplicative identity, $\frac{a}{a}$, where $a$ is not equal to zero. For example, $\frac{3}{4} = \frac{3}{3} \cdot \frac{3}{4} = \frac{3}{4} \cdot \frac{3}{3} = \frac{9}{12}$.

■ When the product of two fractions is equal to 1, the multiplicative identity, the fractions are reciprocals, or multiplicative inverses. For example, $\frac{3}{4}$ and $\frac{4}{3}$ are reciprocals because $\frac{3}{4} \cdot \frac{4}{3} = 1$.

■ To find the reciprocal of a mixed number, you should first write it as an improper fraction. For example, to find the reciprocal of $2\frac{3}{4}$, first write it as $\frac{11}{4}$. The reciprocal is $\frac{4}{11}$.

## Model and Patterns of Fraction Multiplication

■ Finding the area of a rectangle is one model of the multiplication of fractions. The length and width of a rectangle can be proper or improper fractions or mixed numbers.

■ When two positive proper fractions are multiplied, the product is less than either fraction. When two positive improper fractions or mixed numbers are multiplied, the product is greater than or equal to both of the factors.

■ Simplify products by factoring either before or after multiplying. For example, you might find $\frac{4}{5} \cdot \frac{5}{8} = \frac{20}{40}$. This can be simplified to $\frac{1}{2}$. You might also simplify (or cancel) before multiplying. $\frac{4}{5} \cdot \frac{5}{8} = \frac{\cancel{4}}{\cancel{5}} \cdot \frac{\cancel{5}}{2 \cdot \cancel{4}} = \frac{1}{2}$. This might also be written as $\frac{4}{5} \cdot \frac{5}{8} = \frac{\cancel{4}}{\cancel{5}} \cdot \frac{\cancel{5}}{\cancel{8}2} = \frac{1}{2}$.

---

### MATHEMATICALLY SPEAKING

Do you know what these mathematical terms mean?

▶ distributive property of multiplication over addition    ▶ multiplicative inverse    ▶ reciprocal

▶ identity for multiplication (multiplicative identity)    ▶ product

# Study Guide

**Multiplying Fractions**

## Part 1. What did you learn?

1. Copy and complete the table below.

|   | Repeated Addition | Multiplication |
|---|---|---|
| **a.** |  | $2 \cdot \frac{3}{4}$ |
| **b.** | $\frac{3}{5} + \frac{3}{5} + \frac{3}{5} + \frac{3}{5}$ |  |
| **c.** |  | $3 \cdot 1\frac{1}{2}$ |

2. Match the situation with the most appropriate model and expression.

| Situation | Model | Expression |
|---|---|---|
| **a.** Marcy bought 8 bags of raisins. Each bag weighed $\frac{3}{4}$ pound. How many pounds of raisins did Marcy buy? | **e.** | **i.** $12 \cdot \frac{2}{3}$ |
| **b.** Nina bought 12 yards of wire to re-string her guitar. So far she has used $\frac{2}{3}$ of it. How many yards of wire has Nina used? | **f.** | **j.** $8 \cdot \frac{3}{4}$ |
| **c.** Da Un bought 8 apples. She used $\frac{3}{4}$ of them to make a pie. How many apples did Da Un use to make her pie? | **g.** | **k.** $\frac{3}{4} \cdot 8$ |
| **d.** Fredo ran $\frac{2}{3}$ of a mile each day for 12 days. How far did he run in total? | **h.** | **l.** $\frac{2}{3} \cdot 12$ |

3. Use the distributive property of multiplication over addition to find each product.

   **a)** $6 \cdot 2\frac{2}{3}$

   **b)** $24 \cdot 1\frac{1}{8}$

   **c)** $16 \cdot 10\frac{3}{4}$

**4.** Fill in each blank with *greater than, less than* or *between.*

a) If two factors are greater than 0 but less than 1, their product will be _____ 1.

b) If one factor is greater than 0 but less than 1 and the other is greater than 1, their product will be _____ both factors.

c) If two factors are greater than 1, their product will be _____ either factor.

**5.** Logan made a banner to advertise his school's car wash. The dimensions of the banner are $\frac{2}{3}$ foot by $6\frac{1}{2}$ feet. Is the area of the banner more or less than $6\frac{1}{2}$ square feet? How do you know?

**6.** Diondra deposited $\frac{3}{4}$ of her weekly paycheck into her two bank accounts. She put $\frac{2}{3}$ of the deposit into her savings account and the rest in her checking account. Use an equation to show what fraction of the paycheck Diondra deposited in her savings account.

**7.** Fill in the blanks: Two numbers whose product is _____₁ are called reciprocals. The reciprocal of a number is also called its _____₂ . When you _____₃ a number by its inverse, the _____₄ is 1, the _____₅ for multiplication.

**8.** Solve $4 \cdot \frac{3}{4}$ in each of the following ways:

a) On a number line

b) Using repeated addition

c) Using a multiplication algorithm

**9.** Use cancelation to find each of the following products. One example has been done for you.

$$\frac{2}{3} \cdot \frac{3}{4} = \frac{2 \cdot 3}{3 \cdot 4} = \frac{3 \cdot 2}{3 \cdot 4} = \frac{\cancel{3} \cdot \cancel{2}}{\cancel{3} \cdot \cancel{4}2} = \frac{1}{2}$$

a) $\frac{2}{5} \cdot \frac{10}{11}$

b) $\frac{7}{8} \cdot \frac{4}{5}$

c) $1\frac{3}{10} \cdot 6\frac{2}{3}$

d) $5\frac{1}{4} \cdot 2\frac{2}{7}$

10. Show how the multiplicative identity can be used to create an equivalent expression for each of the following: Then, use the multiplicative identity to simplify each expression.

   a) $\frac{3}{4} \cdot \frac{4}{7}$

   b) $1\frac{2}{3} \cdot \frac{2}{5}$

11. If the entire square below represents 1 square unit, use multiplication to find the area of the shaded rectangle.

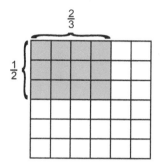

12. If each small square in the diagram below represents $\frac{1}{9}$ square unit, use a multiplication equation to find the area of the entire rectangle.

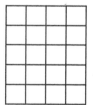

## Part 2. What went wrong?

13. Jimmie tried to use the simplification method he learned in class to multiply $2\frac{3}{4} \cdot \frac{8}{9}$. Here is what he wrote:

   $$2\frac{3}{4} \cdot \frac{8}{9} = 2\frac{3}{4} \cdot \frac{8}{9} = 2\frac{2}{3}$$

   Where did Jimmy go wrong? What would you say or do to help Jimmy find and fix his error?

# Division of Fractions

When you divide whole numbers, the quotient (the answer to a division problem) is less than or equal to the dividend (the number that is divided by another). (In the problem 12 ÷ 3 = 4, 12 is the dividend, 3 is the divisor, and 4 is the quotient.)

With fraction divisors, the results can be quite surprising. In this section, you will explore, estimate and compute using division where one or more of the numbers are fractions or mixed numbers.

 **LESSON 2.1** Dividing by a Whole Number

**MATHEMATICALLY SPEAKING**

▶ quotient
▶ dividend
▶ divisor

 **Start It Off**

Here is a fact family for whole number multiplication and division:

$$3 \cdot 4 = 12 \quad 4 \cdot 3 = 12 \quad 12 \div 3 = 4 \quad 12 \div 4 = 3$$

Here is a fact family for fraction multiplication and division:

$$\frac{3}{7} \cdot \frac{4}{5} = \frac{12}{35} \quad \frac{4}{5} \cdot \frac{3}{7} = \frac{12}{35} \quad \frac{12}{35} \div \frac{3}{7} = \frac{4}{5} \quad \frac{12}{35} \div \frac{4}{5} = \frac{3}{7}$$

In Questions 1 and 2, one equation in a fact family is given. Write the other three equations in each family.

1. $\frac{1}{2} \cdot \frac{3}{4} = \frac{3}{8}$

2. $\frac{8}{15} \div \frac{2}{5} = \frac{4}{3}$

3. How are multiplication and division related?

When you share pizza among friends or form equal-sized teams for basketball, you are using division. In the first two lessons in this section, you will explore sharing division problems in which you know a total amount and the number of groups. The solutions to these division problems are the sizes of each group. There are also measurement division problems in which you know a total amount and the size of each group and have to find the related number of groups. You will begin your exploration of measurement division problems in Lesson 3.

## How Big Is Each Group?

Luke continued to study the old math book he had found. One problem read:

"Mr. Allen had $\$\frac{3}{4}$ for his three daughters' allowance. Each daughter got the same amount."

Luke still thought it was strange to show cents as a fraction of a dollar instead of as a decimal, but it made him think. Luke and his brothers, Matt and John, always got the same amount for their allowances. Luke thought, "Our dad needs $15 for our allowances. He splits that equally 3 ways. I can take $\frac{1}{3}$ of $15, solve $15 ÷ 3$, or think $3 \cdot \underline{\hspace{1cm}} = \$15$ to find how much we each should get."

1. Talk to a partner about how to find the allowance that each of Mr. Allen's three daughters should get if they split $\$\frac{3}{4}$. Use fractions, and draw a diagram to support your answer.

In the book, the Allen sisters thought that their friends got bigger allowances than they did. They asked their friends how much money their families spent on allowances and recorded the amounts in a chart.

2. Use what you know about fractions to estimate whether their friends would get a larger, smaller or the same allowance as the Allen sisters. Be prepared to explain your reasoning.

| | Family | Total Allowance to Split Evenly Among All Children | Number of Children | Estimate: Allowance Is Greater Than, Less Than or Equal to Allen Sisters' Allowance |
|---|---|---|---|---|
| a) | Allens | $\$\frac{3}{4}$ | 3 | |
| b) | Bowens | $\$\frac{4}{5}$ | 4 | |
| c) | Cooks | $\$\frac{3}{5}$ | 6 | |
| d) | Davidsons | $\$\frac{9}{10}$ | 3 | |
| e) | Earnharts | $\$\frac{4}{5}$ | 5 | |
| f) | Franks | $\$\frac{1}{2}$ | 2 | |

3. Luke's classmates made the following claims about the allowances. State whether you agree or disagree and give your reasons using words and/or diagrams.

   a) Each child in one family got the same allowance as each of the Allen sisters.

   b) The Earnhart children each got $\$\frac{1}{5}$, which is less than $\$\frac{1}{4}$.

   c) Each child in only one family got a greater allowance than each of the Allen sisters.

The Allen sisters said that they could find that each of their own allowances was $\$\frac{1}{4}$ by multiplying $\frac{1}{3} \cdot \$\frac{3}{4}$, dividing $\$\frac{3}{4} \div 3$, or solving $3 \cdot \underline{\hspace{1cm}} = \$\frac{3}{4}$.

4. Copy and complete the chart to find the allowance that each child should get if each family's total is split evenly. Use diagrams and equations to help you find the exact allowance. Write the allowance as a fraction of a dollar.

| Family | Total Allowance to Split Evenly Among All Children | Number of Children | Multiplication Equation Showing Allowance for Each Child | Division Equation Showing Allowance for Each Child |
|---|---|---|---|---|
| a) Allens | $\$\frac{3}{4}$ | 3 | $\frac{1}{3} \cdot \$\frac{3}{4} = \$\frac{1}{4}$ or $3 \cdot \$\frac{1}{4} = \$\frac{3}{4}$ | $\$\frac{3}{4} \div 3 = \$\frac{1}{4}$ |
| b) Bowens | $\$\frac{4}{5}$ | 4 | | |
| c) Cooks | $\$\frac{3}{5}$ | 6 | | |
| d) Davidsons | $\$\frac{9}{10}$ | 3 | | |
| e) Earnharts | $\$\frac{4}{5}$ | 5 | | |
| f) Franks | $\$\frac{1}{2}$ | 2 | | |

**g)** What property says that $\frac{1}{3} \cdot \frac{3}{4} = \frac{3}{4} \cdot \frac{1}{3}$?

5. Convert each allowance to dollars and cents. Did you correctly estimate which children's allowances were greater than, less than or equal to the Allen sisters' allowances?

6. In the United States, money amounts are not usually written as a fraction, but many other quantities are. Show your work with diagrams, words and/or equations in solving each of the following:

   **a)** Three people are sharing a $\frac{3}{4}$-pound box of popcorn. If they share equally, how much popcorn does each person get?

   **b)** The pizza parlor has $\frac{4}{5}$ pound of cheese to split evenly on two pizzas. How much cheese will be on each pizza?

   **c)** $\frac{3}{6}$ cup of rice is used to make rice pudding for three people. How much rice is needed to make rice pudding for one person?

   **d)** Write your own word problem for $\frac{3}{5} \div 3$. Include the solution. Trade with a friend, solve and compare solutions.

In Question 6, you may have noticed that when you divide a fraction by a whole number, you can just divide the numerator by the whole number.

> **Example**
>
> To find the quotient of $\frac{3}{4} \div 3$, you could find $\frac{3 \div 3}{4} = \frac{1}{4}$.

Dividing by a whole number is the same as multiplying by the unit fraction that is the reciprocal of that whole number.

To find the quotient of $\frac{3}{4} \div 3$, you could find $\frac{1}{3} \cdot \frac{3}{4}$ and get $\frac{3}{12}$.

This simplifies to $\frac{1}{4}$, which is the same solution you would find by dividing the numerator by 3.

7. Solve by multiplying the dividend by the reciprocal of the divisor. Then solve by dividing the numerator of the dividend by the whole number divisor.

**a)**

| Expression | Multiply the Dividend by the Reciprocal of the Divisor | Divide the Numerator by the Divisor |
|---|---|---|
| $\frac{3}{5} \div 3$ | $\frac{1}{3} \cdot \frac{3}{5} = $ _____ | $\frac{3 \div 3}{5} = $ _____ |
| $\frac{12}{15} \div 4$ | | |
| $\frac{9}{10} \div 3$ | | |
| $\frac{3}{5} \div 4$ | | |

**b)** Did you get the same answers using both methods?

**c)** In words, explain how you solved $\frac{3}{5} \div 4$ by dividing the numerator by 4.

 **Hint**
See page 146

**d)** Which method do you prefer? Why?

**e)** Choose one of the expressions, write a word problem and draw a diagram to show that your answer makes sense. Share your work with a partner.

# Sharing Mixed Numbers

Matt, Luke and John Anderson also thought that all their friends had greater allowances than they did. Matt tried to convince their father to raise their allowances. Their father said that he would raise their total family allowance to $17.25 a week if the three boys shared it equally. Matt used mixed numbers to think about sharing the money. He told his brothers that they would share a total allowance of $17\frac{1}{4}$.

8. Talk to a partner about the amount that each brother should get.

    a) Estimate the amount each boy should get.

    b) Find the exact amount. Use equations and diagrams to explain your thinking.

The Anderson brothers surveyed their friends to compare allowances. They recorded the total allowance as a mixed number and noted the number of children splitting it in each family.

9. Estimate which children get greater allowances than the Anderson brothers. Be prepared to discuss your reasoning.

| | Family | Total Allowance to Split Evenly Among All Children | Number of Children | Estimate: Greater than the Andersons? |
|---|---|---|---|---|
| a) | Andersons | $17\frac{1}{4}$ | 3 | ✕ |
| b) | Browns | $15\frac{1}{5}$ | 3 | |
| c) | Cowans | $40\frac{4}{5}$ | 6 | |
| d) | Deerings | $5\frac{1}{2}$ | 1 | |
| e) | Edgells | $22 | 4 | |

10. Choose your own method to find the allowance for each child. Then copy and complete the chart to determine which children get greater allowances than the Anderson brothers. Be prepared to discuss your method.

| | Family | Total Allowance to Split Evenly Among All Children | Number of Children | Multiplication Equation Showing Allowance for Each Child | Division Equation Showing Allowance for Each Child |
|---|---|---|---|---|---|
| a) | Andersons | $17\frac{1}{4}$ | 3 | $\frac{1}{3} \cdot \$17\frac{1}{4} = \$5\frac{3}{4}$ or $3 \cdot \$5\frac{3}{4} = \$17\frac{1}{4}$ | $\$17\frac{1}{4} \div 3 = \$5\frac{3}{4}$ |
| b) | Browns | $15\frac{1}{5}$ | 3 | | |
| c) | Cowans | $40\frac{4}{5}$ | 6 | | |
| d) | Deerings | $5\frac{1}{2}$ | 1 | | |
| e) | Edgells | $22 | 4 | | |

    f) Choose one of the families with more than one child and draw a diagram to show each child's allowance. How does this relate to your equations?

One way to divide a mixed number by a whole number is to use the distributive property of division over addition. For example, to divide $13\frac{1}{2}$ by 4, you could first write $13\frac{1}{2}$ as $12 + 1 + \frac{1}{2}$ since 12 is a multiple of 4. The equation then becomes:

$$13\frac{1}{2} \div 4 = \left(12 + 1 + \frac{1}{2}\right) \div 4 = (12 \div 4) + (1 \div 4) + \left(\frac{1}{2} \div 4\right) =$$
$$3 + \frac{1}{4} + \frac{1}{8} = 3\frac{3}{8}.$$

Another way to divide a mixed number by a whole number is to convert the mixed number to an equivalent improper fraction before dividing by the whole number.

$$13\frac{1}{2} \div 4 = \frac{27}{2} \div 4 = \frac{1}{4} \cdot \frac{27}{2} = \frac{27}{8} = 3\frac{3}{8}$$

**g)** Try one or both of these methods for Parts a–e. How do your answers compare to the values in your chart?

**11.** Write a situation that could be solved using each of the following expressions. Draw a diagram and write an equation for each situation. Show your work.

**a)** $\frac{8}{15} \div 4$                          **b)** $12\frac{3}{4} \div 3$

## ⬆W rap It Up

**MATHEMATICALLY SPEAKING**

▶ dividend

▶ divisor

▶ quotient

When dividing a proper or improper fraction by a whole number, you can either divide the numerator of the fraction by the whole number or multiply the fraction by the reciprocal of the whole number. Talk to a partner about why this works. Create a situation and a diagram for each of the following expressions.

$\frac{4}{5} \div 2$                  $12\frac{1}{2} \div 5$

LESSON
2.1 SECTION 2

On Your Own

MATERIALS LIST

▶ Lesson Guide 2.1:
   On Your Own

Write
About It

1. Explain in words and with a diagram why dividing by a whole number has the same effect as multiplying by its reciprocal. Use $\frac{4}{5} \div 8$ and $13\frac{1}{2} \div 3$ as examples.

2. $\frac{4}{5} \div 8$ may be thought of as $\frac{1}{8} \cdot \frac{4}{5}$. Why is $\frac{1}{8} \cdot \frac{4}{5}$ the same as $\frac{4}{5} \cdot \frac{1}{8}$?

3. When Mr. Allen's three daughters got their allowances, their father also gave them a half-pound of almonds. Use a number line and a bar diagram to show what part of a pound each girl should get if the sisters split the almonds evenly.

4. Brothers Matt, Luke and John had to mow the lawn. They planned to each mow the same amount. The lawn measured $\frac{9}{10}$ of an acre.

   a) Luke estimated that they each had less than $\frac{1}{2}$ acre to mow. Was Luke correct? Explain.

   b) How much should each brother mow? Draw a bar diagram or number line, and write a multiplication or division equation to show your work.

   c) For each of the following lawns, determine how much each person should mow if they split the mowing evenly. Write one multiplication and one division equation for each.

| Size of Lawn to be Mowed, in Acres | Number of People Mowing | Multiplication Equation | Division Equation |
|---|---|---|---|
| $\frac{6}{7}$ | 3 | | |
| $\frac{8}{9}$ | 4 | | |
| $\frac{6}{8}$ | 2 | | |
| $\frac{3}{4}$ | 2 | | |

5. Ms. Jones has $\frac{2}{3}$ pound of lunchmeat to split evenly among four sandwiches. How much meat is in each sandwich?

   a) Write and solve a multiplication equation and a division equation to find the amount of meat in each sandwich.

   b) Draw a diagram to show how you found your answer.

**6.** Monica has $3\frac{3}{4}$ yards of ribbon to split equally on six wrapped presents. How much ribbon will be on each present?

**7.** Estimate the value for each expression, and then solve using a multiplication equation and a division equation. Use the method of your choice.

| Expression | Estimate | Multiplication Equation | Division Equation |
|---|---|---|---|
| **a)** $14\frac{2}{5} \div 5$ | | | |
| **b)** $72\frac{1}{2} \div 10$ | | | |
| **c)** $26\frac{1}{4} \div 8$ | | | |
| **d)** $32\frac{2}{3} \div 4$ | | | |

**8.** Aiden works at a pet store. He gives each animal the same amount of food. How much will each one get? Show your work.

   **a)** $\frac{3}{4}$ pound of carrots to feed six rabbits

   **b)** $5\frac{1}{3}$ ounces of parsley to feed eight gerbils

   **c)** $\frac{3}{5}$ pound of birdseed to feed nine parrots

**9.** A grocery store receipt shows the following. What was the price for 1 pound of each item?

   **a)** $2\frac{1}{4}$ for 3 pounds of bananas

   **b)** $5\frac{3}{5}$ for 2 pounds of strawberries

   **c)** $3\frac{1}{5}$ for a 4-pound chicken

**10.** Answer the following questions from Luke's old math book. He earned the same amount each day. Show your work. Use estimation to see if your answers make sense.

   **a)** Mr. B earned $35\frac{1}{8}$ by working 8 days. He earned the same amount each day. How much did he earn in one day?

   **b)** I paid $10\frac{1}{8}$ for 27 pounds of butter. What did I pay for one pound?

   **c)** A farmer received $233\frac{1}{2}$ for 21 bushels of clover seed. How much did he get for one bushel?

 Think
Beyond

11. Show how you could divide three identical square sandwiches equally among five people with as few cuts as possible. How much does each person get? What might each share look like? How many cuts does it take?

 Hint
See page 146

 Think
Beyond

12. In 2004, Sonya Thomas set a world record by eating $8\frac{2}{5}$ pounds of baked beans in $2\frac{3}{4}$ minutes. If she ate at a steadily rate, how many pounds of baked beans did she eat each minute? Show your work.

 Think
Back

13. Complete the table with equivalent fractions, decimals and percents.

| Fraction in Simplest Form | Decimal | Percent |
|:---:|:---:|:---:|
| $\frac{3}{8}$ | | |
| | 0.75 | |
| | | $12\frac{1}{2}\%$ |
| $\frac{5}{6}$ | | |

14. Use what you know about multiplying and dividing by powers of ten to complete the following:

a) $45 \cdot 100 =$ _____

b) $5,700 \div$ _____ $= 57$

c) $375,000 \div 100 =$ _____

d) $2,500 \div 50 =$ _____

e) $210 \div$ _____ $= 3$

15. A gross is a dozen dozens. How many items are in each of the following amounts:

a) 1 gross

b) 5 gross

c) $\frac{1}{3}$ gross

d) $2\frac{5}{6}$ gross

e) $6\frac{3}{4}$ gross

16. Look at the following shapes. List all the shapes in each category.

**Hint**
See page 146

a) Parallelograms

b) Trapezoids

c) Rectangles

d) Quadrilaterals

i)

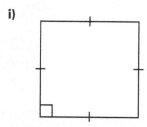

iv)

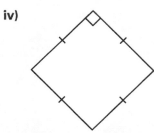

ii)

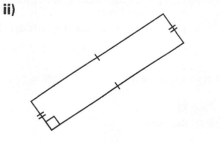

v)

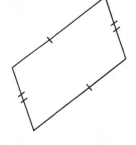

iii)

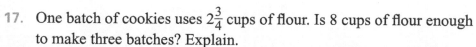

vi)

17. One batch of cookies uses $2\frac{3}{4}$ cups of flour. Is 8 cups of flour enough to make three batches? Explain.

# Dividing by a Fraction

## → Start It Off

Elisa says that if you multiply a dividend and a divisor by the same number, the quotient stays the same. For example:

$$48 \div 6 = 8$$
$$\times 10 \quad \times 10$$
$$480 \div 60 = 8$$

1. Elisa said $30 \div 5 = 6$, so $90 \div 15 = 6$. By what number did Elisa multiply the dividend and divisor in the first equation to get the second equation?

2. Start with $16 \div 4$ and multiply both numbers by 3. What is your new problem? Do both problems have the same quotient?

3. Make up another division problem and multiply the dividend and the divisor by the same number. Do both problems have the same quotient?

 **Think Beyond**

4. Why do these pairs of division expressions have the same quotient?

    **Hint**
   **See page 146**

5. Start with $5 \div \frac{1}{4}$. Multiply the dividend and the divisor each by 4. What is the quotient of the new expression? What is $5 \div \frac{1}{4}$?

Solve the following by first multiplying the dividend and the divisor each by the same number. Show your work.

6. $7 \div \frac{1}{3} = $ _____

7. $6 \div \frac{1}{5} = $ _____

In this lesson, you will continue to explore sharing division problems where you know a total and a number of groups, and you have to find the amount in each group. The only difference between the division problems in this lesson and those in the last lesson is that, instead of a whole number of groups, you now will work with a fractional part of a group. You are still finding the size of, or amount in, one group.

Misha loves to cook. She works with fractions whenever she is baking.

1. Misha plans to make cookies.

   **a)** Misha has 5 cups of sugar, which is enough to make three batches of cookies. How might she find the number of cups of sugar needed for one batch? Write a division equation and a multiplication equation to show this and complete the diagram.

   | 1 batch = _____ cups | 1 batch = _____ cups | 1 batch =_____ cups |
   |---|---|---|
   | 5 cups of sugar | | |

   **b)** If 2 cups of sugar is enough to make $\frac{1}{3}$ of a large batch of another type of cookies, how many cups are needed for one batch of those cookies? An equation for this might be $2 \div \frac{1}{3} = n$ or $3 \cdot 2 = n$ or $\frac{1}{3} \cdot n = 2$. Draw a diagram to illustrate your solution. Compare this to your answers to Part a.

   **c)** Misha uses 2 cups of sugar to make $\frac{2}{3}$ of a batch of a third type of cookies. How much sugar is needed for one batch? Write a division equation and a multiplication equation to represent this and complete the diagram.

   | 2 cups sugar for $\frac{2}{3}$ batch | | |
   |---|---|---|
   | _____ cup for $\frac{1}{3}$ batch | _____ cup for $\frac{1}{3}$ batch | |
   | ? cups for 1 batch | | |

   Draw and label a diagram and write one multiplication equation and one division equation to answer each of the following questions.

   **d)** If 6 cups of sugar is enough for $\frac{3}{4}$ of a large batch of one type of cookie, how much sugar is needed for one batch?

   **e)** $\frac{3}{4}$ tsp. of vanilla is enough for $\frac{1}{2}$ batch of cookies. How much vanilla is needed for one batch?

   **f)** If 1 tsp. of vanilla is enough for $\frac{2}{3}$ batch of cookies, how much vanilla is needed for a whole batch?

   **g)** Misha has $\frac{3}{4}$ tsp. of vanilla. This is enough for $\frac{2}{3}$ batch of cookies. How much vanilla would she need for a whole batch?

   **h)** Explain why each of these problems is a sharing division problem.

Misha said that when she has 32 ounces of butter, she can make 4 batches of cookies. To find the number of ounces of butter needed for one batch, she could divide 32 by 4, find $\frac{1}{4}$ of 32, or solve for the missing factor in the multiplication problem $4 \cdot \underline{\hspace{1cm}} = 32$. Gerrard wanted Misha's recipe for chocolate chip cookies. Instead of giving Gerrard the recipe, Misha challenged him to find the recipe using the following table.

2. **a)** Work with a partner to find the amount of each ingredient Gerrard will need for one batch of chocolate chip cookies. Draw diagrams if needed. Be prepared to explain your reasoning.

| Total Amount of Ingredient on Hand | Number of Batches It Will Make | Division Equation to Find Amount Needed for 1 Batch | Multiplication Equation to Find Amount Needed for 1 Batch |
|---|---|---|---|
| 32 ounces butter | 4 | $32 \div 4 = \frac{32}{4} = 8$ oz. | $\frac{1}{4} \cdot 32 = \frac{32}{4} = 8$ oz. |
| 3 cups white sugar | 4 | | |
| 6 cups brown sugar | 8 | | |
| $\frac{2}{3}$ teaspoon baking soda | $\frac{2}{3}$ | | |
| $4\frac{1}{2}$ cups flour | 2 | | |
| 3 eggs | $\frac{3}{2}$ | | |
| 6 teaspoons vanilla | 3 | | |
| $\frac{1}{3}$ cup chocolate chips | $\frac{1}{6}$ | | |
| $\frac{1}{4}$ teaspoon salt | $\frac{1}{2}$ | | |

**b)** Compare the division and multiplication equations for each ingredient. Use the terms *reciprocals* and *inverse operations* in your comparison.

# Making Sense

When you divide by a number greater than 1, the quotient is less than the dividend. When you divide by a number less than 1, the quotient is greater than the dividend. In this section, you will explore why this is the case.

Nicholas works in a grocery store after school. He said that $\frac{1}{4}$ of a box holds 6 cans. He wondered if he could use division to find the number of cans that one box will hold.

3. Talk to a partner about how you might use division to find the number of cans that one box will hold.

  a) How many cans will fit in one box? Show the division equation.

  b) Write a multiplication equation to show this situation.

  c) What if 6 cans fill $\frac{3}{4}$ of another box? Draw a diagram to show the number of cans that this box will hold. Explain how the equation $6 \div \frac{3}{4} = n$ fits this situation.

  d) Darrin said that he solved $6 \div \frac{3}{4} = n$ using $(\frac{1}{3} \cdot 6) \cdot 4 = n$. Explain how this multiplication sentence fits this situation.

  e) Compare the division equation in Part c to the multiplication equation in Part d. Use the terms *reciprocals* and *inverse operations* in your comparison.

4. Jamela has painted $\frac{1}{3}$ of one bedroom wall in $\frac{3}{4}$ of 1 hour. At this rate, how long will it take Jamela to paint the whole wall?

  a) Explain how the equation $\frac{3}{4} \div \frac{1}{3} = n$ fits this situation.

  b) Write and solve a multiplication equation to find how long it would take Jamela to paint one whole wall.

  c) What if it takes Jamela $\frac{3}{4}$ of an hour to paint $\frac{2}{3}$ of another wall? Write a division equation to describe this situation. Draw a diagram to show how long it would take Jamela to paint one whole wall.

  d) Explain how you might solve this using $(\frac{1}{2} \cdot \frac{3}{4}) \cdot 3 = n$.

  e) Compare the division equation in Part c to the multiplication equation in Part d. Use the terms *reciprocals* and *inverse operations* in your comparison.

5. $1\frac{1}{2}$ pounds of peanuts costs $\$1\frac{4}{5}$.

   a) How would you find the cost of $\frac{1}{2}$ pound of peanuts? How could you use that answer to find the cost of 1 pound of peanuts?

   b) Write and solve a division equation to find the cost of 1 pound of peanuts. Show your work with a diagram or numbers.

   c) Write a multiplication equation for the same situation.

   d) How is dividing by a mixed number related to multiplying by its reciprocal?

6. For each of the following:

   • Write a sharing word problem that could be solved using the given equation. Remember that you are solving for the amount in one group.

   • Show your solution with a diagram or model.

   • Write a multiplication equation for the same situation.

   a) $2 \div \frac{1}{3} = n$

   b) $3 \div 1\frac{1}{2} = n$

   c) $\frac{3}{5} \div \frac{2}{3} = n$

   d) How do your multiplication equations compare to your division equations? Does multiplying the dividend by the reciprocal of the divisor give the same solution as solving the original division problem?

 **W rap It Up**

Jalil said that he could solve $1\frac{1}{3} \div \frac{4}{5} = n$ by multiplying $1\frac{1}{3}$ by the reciprocal of $\frac{4}{5}$. Talk to a partner about whether Jalil is correct. Write a word problem that could be solved by using Jalil's equation. Use numbers, words and diagrams in your explanation.

LESSON
2.2 SECTION 2

On Your Own

MATERIALS LIST
▶ Lesson Guide 2.2:
   On Your Own

**Write About It**

1. Write a sharing word problem that can be solved by using $1\frac{1}{2} \div \frac{3}{4} = n$.

   a) Draw a diagram that shows your solution.

   b) Write a multiplication equation that can be used to solve the same problem. How does your multiplication equation compare to the division equation?

   c) Using your equations and diagram, explain why the quotient in a division problem is not always smaller than the dividend.

2. Copy and complete the following chart to find the ingredients needed for 1 batch of brownies. Show your work.

| Total Amount of Ingredient | Number of Batches It Will Make | Amount Needed for 1 Batch |
|---|---|---|
| 8 ounces unsweetened chocolate | $1\frac{3}{5}$ | |
| $\frac{2}{3}$ cup vegetable oil | 2 | |
| $\frac{3}{4}$ cup sugar | $\frac{3}{4}$ | |
| $\frac{1}{2}$ egg | $\frac{1}{4}$ | |
| 3 cups flour | 4 | |
| $\frac{1}{4}$ teaspoon baking powder | $\frac{1}{2}$ | |
| $\frac{1}{3}$ teaspoon salt | $\frac{2}{3}$ | |

3. Bella's mom said that to solve problems like $\frac{1}{3} \div \frac{4}{5} = n$, she learned: "Ours is not to reason why. Just invert and multiply."

   a) What do you think she meant? How would she solve the equation for $n$?

   b) Help Bella explain to her mother why this works.

4. A grocery store receipt showed the following. What was the price for 1 pound of each item?

   a) $3\frac{1}{5}$ for $\frac{4}{5}$ pound of ham

   b) $1\frac{3}{4}$ for $\frac{7}{8}$ pound of peanuts

   c) $2\frac{2}{5}$ for $\frac{2}{3}$ pound of cheese

   d) $4\frac{1}{5}$ for $1\frac{3}{4}$ pounds of bologna

**5.** $1\frac{2}{3}$ meters of wire weighs 12 grams. How much would 1 meter of wire weigh?

**6.** Katya can walk $2\frac{3}{4}$ miles in $\frac{4}{5}$ of an hour. At this rate, how far can she walk in 1 hour?

**7.** $2\frac{1}{2}$ pounds of cheese is enough to make sandwiches for $\frac{3}{4}$ of the class. How many pounds of cheese would it take to make sandwiches for the whole class?

**8.** In 1877, $\frac{3}{4}$ of an acre of land cost $108.

   **a)** At this rate, what would 1 acre of land cost?

   **b)** At the same rate, what would $\frac{2}{3}$ of an acre cost?

**9.** In 1878, Mr. Lincoln made a first payment of $\frac{2}{3}$ of the purchase price of a house. His first payment was $2,480.

   **a)** What was the purchase price of the house?

   **b)** If he had only needed to make a first payment of $\frac{1}{5}$ of the purchase price, what would the first payment have been?

**10.** If $\frac{2}{3}$ of the purchase price of a house today is $150,286 what is the purchase price of the house?

**Think Beyond**

**11.** Using equations, show that $\frac{a}{b} \div \frac{c}{d} = \frac{a}{b} \cdot \frac{d}{c}$.

**Think Back**

**12.** The radius of a circle is 2.6 cm. What is the diameter?

**13.** Find the area and the perimeter of the isosceles trapezoid.

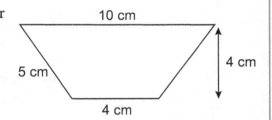

**14.** Today Jenna spent $6\frac{1}{2}$ hours in school and $1\frac{3}{4}$ hours on homework. How much total time did Jenna spend in school and on homework?

**15.** Together, Kiera and Joel have $9.39. Joel has twice as much money as Kiera. How much money does Kiera have?

**16.** How many sides does a decagon have?

   **A.** 6          **B.** 8          **C.** 10          **D.** 12

# LESSON 2.3 More Fraction Division

## Start It Off

The expression 6 ÷ 2 can represent the number of loaves of bread you can make if you have 6 cups of flour and each loaf needs 2 cups of flour. This is an example of grouping division, in which you know a total and the size of each group and you need to find the number of groups. A different meaning might be that 6 cups of flour is enough for 2 loaves of bread. You need to find the number of cups of flour needed for one loaf. This is an example of sharing division, in which you know a total and the number or parts of groups and you need to find the size of each group.

Write a grouping division problem and a sharing division problem for $\frac{3}{4} \div \frac{1}{4}$. Be prepared to explain your method of solution for each.

In the first two lessons in this section, the division problems were all sharing division problems. In this section, you will explore grouping division problems. Both types of division can be compared to multiplication equations with a missing factor.

## Measuring with Fractions

The students at Sharp Middle School are making food baskets. Murtaza has 1 pound of grapes, and he puts $\frac{1}{8}$ pound in each basket. He thought, "I know that 1 pound is the same as $\frac{8}{8}$ pound. I have to figure how many $\frac{1}{8}$s are in $\frac{8}{8}$." He drew the following to find the number of baskets in which he could put a total of 1 pound of grapes.

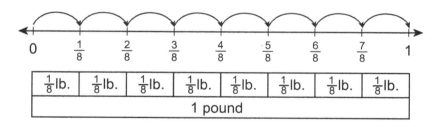

Murtaza wrote $\frac{8}{8} \div \frac{1}{8} = 8$ to show his solution.

1. Talk to a partner about the number of baskets Murtaza could fill if he puts $\frac{1}{8}$ pound in each basket and has the following total amounts of grapes. Write an equation and use a number line or bar diagram to show your solution.

   **a)** $\frac{3}{8}$ pound

   **b)** 5 pounds

   **c)** $\frac{1}{2}$ pound

   **d)** $3\frac{3}{4}$ pounds

Murtaza said that he could find the number of baskets in Question 1a by using subtraction. Starting with $\frac{3}{8}$, he repeatedly subtracts $\frac{1}{8}$.

$$\frac{3}{8} - \frac{1}{8} = \frac{2}{8}$$
$$\frac{2}{8} - \frac{1}{8} = \frac{1}{8}$$
$$\frac{1}{8} - \frac{1}{8} = 0$$

He subtracts $\frac{1}{8}$ three times. He can fill three baskets.

2. Show how to use repeated subtraction to find the number of $\frac{1}{8}$s in $\frac{1}{2}$.

When you add or subtract fractions, you first write them with a common denominator. Let's explore whether this method also makes sense when you divide fractions.

3. Look at the problems in Question 1.

   **a)** Write each as a division problem in which the fractions have a common denominator.

   For example, $2 \div \frac{1}{8} = \frac{16}{8} \div \frac{1}{8}$

   **b)** Murtaza said that he could divide straight across just like in multiplication. He wrote $\frac{3}{8} \div \frac{1}{8} = \frac{3 \div 1}{8 \div 8} = \frac{3}{1} = 3$. Divide each of your expressions this way. Compare your answers to the answers in Question 1. What do you notice?

   **c)** Murtaza wondered if this only works with unit fractions. To test this, he wrote $\frac{1}{8}$ as $\frac{2}{16}$ and tried again. Write $\frac{3}{8}$ and $\frac{1}{8}$ as sixteenths and divide straight across. Did you get the same answer?

   **d)** Talk to a partner about why you can divide numerators and denominators straight across when working with fractions that have a common denominator.

   **e)** Divide each of the following straight across. What do you notice? How does this compare to your earlier work with equivalent fractions?

   $$\frac{6}{8} \div \frac{2}{2} \qquad \frac{9}{12} \div \frac{3}{3} \qquad \frac{15}{20} \div \frac{5}{5}$$

**4.** Marci puts $\frac{3}{4}$ pound of peanuts in each basket.

**a)** Draw a diagram to find the number of baskets she can fill with $2\frac{1}{4}$ pounds of peanuts.

**b)** Write a division problem to show the number of baskets she can fill. Use common denominators. Write any mixed number as an improper fraction and divide straight across. Does the quotient match what you found with your diagram?

**c)** How many baskets could Marci fill with $\frac{3}{4}$ pound of peanuts using each of the following total amounts of peanuts? Explain your answers with diagrams and equations. Does the algorithm of dividing numerators and denominators straight across work for these problems?

3 pounds      $1\frac{3}{4}$ pounds      $5\frac{1}{4}$ pounds

---

**Example**

When dividing fractions or mixed numbers, you can use common denominators. Using this method, you can divide going straight across.

$$1\frac{1}{2} \div \frac{3}{10} = \frac{3}{2} \div \frac{3}{10} = \frac{15}{10} \div \frac{3}{10} = \frac{15 \div 3}{10 \div 10} = \frac{5}{1} = 5$$

---

# Making Sense of the Leftovers

Quotients aren't always whole numbers. When you divide 16 by 3, you can write the quotient as 5 with a remainder of 1 or as $5\frac{1}{3}$. For example, if you have 16 pounds of bread and put 3 pounds in each basket, you can use the equation $16 \div 3 = n$ to find the number of baskets you can fill. You can fill 5 baskets, and will have 1 pound left as a remainder. This pound could fill $\frac{1}{3}$ of another basket. So, you can fill 5 baskets with a remainder of 1 pound of bread, or you can fill $5\frac{1}{3}$ baskets.

**5.** Look at the equation $25 \div 4 = n$

**a)** Write a word problem for $n = 6$ with a remainder of 1.

**b)** Write a word problem for $n = 6\frac{1}{4}$.

Let's explore how this relates to fractions.

**6.** Madison has 1 pound of crackers. She puts $\frac{3}{8}$ pound of crackers in each basket.

   **a)** Can Madison fill three baskets? Explain.

   **b)** How many baskets can Madison completely fill?

   **c)** How many pounds of crackers will be left over?

   **d)** What fraction of a basket is this? Draw a diagram to show your solution.

**7.** Montana puts $\frac{2}{3}$ pound of cheese in each basket. She has 3 pounds of cheese.

   **a)** How many baskets can she completely fill?

   **b)** How much cheese will be left over?

   **c)** What fraction of a basket is this? Explain.

Nedda is making birdfeeders. The following chart shows how much birdseed is needed to fill each type of birdfeeder.

| Type of Birdfeeder | Capacity |
|---|---|
| Bluebird feeder | $\frac{3}{4}$ gallon |
| Chickadee feeder | $\frac{3}{16}$ gallon |
| Songbird feeder | $1\frac{1}{2}$ gallons |
| Window bird feeder | $\frac{1}{4}$ gallon |

**8.** If Nedda has 1 gallon of birdseed for each type of feeder, how many times can she fill each feeder? Compare your answers to a partner's. Use words and diagrams to explain your solutions.

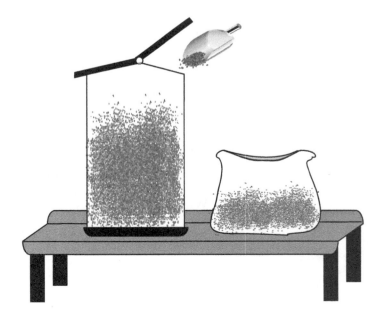

**9.** **a)** Use repeated subtraction to find how many times the chickadee feeder could be completely filled using 1 gallon of birdseed.

    **b)** Will there be any birdseed left after the feeder is filled a whole number of times?

    **c)** What fractional part of the feeder can be filled with the leftover amount?

**10.** Nedda did the following to find how many chickadee feeders she could fill with 1 gallon of birdseed.

$$\frac{3}{16} \overline{\smash{\big)}\, \frac{16}{16}} \begin{array}{c} 5 \\ \end{array}$$

$$\begin{array}{r} \frac{5}{\phantom{0}} \\ \frac{3}{16}\overline{\smash{\big)}\frac{16}{16}} \\ -\ \frac{15}{16} \\ \hline \frac{1}{16} \end{array}$$

    **a)** What number in the problem tells how many complete birdfeeders she could fill?

    **b)** What does the $\frac{1}{16}$ represent?

    **c)** What fraction of a feeder could be filled with the remaining birdseed?

**11.** David told Nedda he could solve the problem using a common denominator.

    He wrote $1 \div \frac{3}{16} = \frac{16}{16} \div \frac{3}{16} = \frac{16 \div 3}{16 \div 16} = \frac{16 \div 3}{1} = 16 \div 3 = 5\frac{1}{3}$

    **a)** Compare David's method to Nedda's. Do they both get the same answer?

    **b)** What does the $\frac{1}{3}$ mean in David's solution?

    **c)** What happens when you divide common denominators straight across? How does this affect your final quotient?

    **d)** Use David's method to find the number of times the other birdfeeders could be filled using 1 gallon of birdseed. Does this match what you found with your diagrams?

**12.** Brianna said that since these were division problems, you should be able to multiply the dividend by the reciprocal of the divisor. She said that to find the number of times the chickadee feeder could be filled, she could use $1 \cdot \frac{16}{3}$ instead of $1 \div \frac{3}{16}$.

**a)** Would Brianna get the same answer for the number of times that the chickadee feeder could be filled?

**b)** Try Brianna's method on the other feeders. Does this method work for all the feeders?

**13.** Solve each of the following using the common denominator algorithm and the multiply by the reciprocal of the divisor algorithm.

| Equation | Common Denominator Algorithm | Reciprocal of the Divisor Algorithm |
|---|---|---|
| **a)** $\frac{3}{8} \div \frac{2}{3} = n$ | | |
| **b)** $n = 1\frac{3}{5} \div 1\frac{1}{2}$ | | |
| **c)** $n = \frac{3}{4} \div \frac{5}{8}$ | | |

**d)** Do both algorithms give you the same quotients?

**e)** What happens to the denominators when you use the common denominator algorithm and divide straight across? How does this affect your final quotient?

**f)** Choose one of the equations, and write a word problem that could be answered by using this equation. Draw a diagram to explain your solution.

 **W rap It Up**

There are two popular algorithms for dividing proper and improper fractions. One is to multiply the dividend by the reciprocal of the divisor (the invert and multiply algorithm). The other is to write the dividend and the divisor as fractions with a common denominator, and then to divide straight across (the common denominator algorithm). Talk to a partner about how these algorithms are similar and how they are different. Use situations, equations and diagrams in your explanations.

**Write About It**

1. When dividing fractions or mixed numbers, you can find a common denominator and divide straight across.

   a) Show how this common denominator algorithm works. Write a word problem that can be solved by finding $1\frac{3}{4} \div \frac{2}{3}$. Use diagrams to explain your answer.

   b) Show how you might find the value of this expression using the reciprocal of the divisor algorithm.

   c) Compare the two algorithms. Which do you prefer and why?

2. Davis says that to find the number of quarters in any number of dollars, you should divide the number of dollars by $\frac{1}{4}$. Christy says that you should multiply by 4. Who is right? Explain.

3. A quarter is sometimes called "two bits" in old movies.

   a) What part of a dollar is one bit? Show this using division.

   b) How many bits are in $\$\frac{1}{2}$? How many bits are in $\$2\frac{3}{4}$?

4. It takes Jane $\frac{1}{6}$ minute to recite the alphabet. How many times can she recite it in $1\frac{1}{2}$ minutes?

5. Complete the following table by dividing the first number in each row by the fraction at the top of each column. What patterns do you notice?

| $\div$ | $\frac{1}{4}$ | $\frac{2}{4}$ | $\frac{4}{4}$ |
|---|---|---|---|
| 4 | | | |
| 2 | | | |
| 1 | | | |

6. Sam is building a 10-foot-long wall.

   a) Stones are each $\frac{1}{3}$ foot long. How many stones would Sam need for each row of the wall?

   b) Bricks are each $\frac{2}{3}$ foot long. How many bricks would Sam need for each row of the wall?

   c) How do your answers to Parts a and b compare? Explain.

   d) What if Sam made the wall with cement blocks that are each $1\frac{1}{3}$ feet long? Predict the number of blocks he would he need for each row. Check your prediction using division.

7. On a recent national test, only 55% of eighth grade students answered the following question correctly. Explain what the correct answer is.

   Jim has $\frac{3}{4}$ yard of string. He wants to cut it into pieces that are each $\frac{1}{8}$ yard long.

   How many pieces will he have?

8. Remainders can be rewritten as a fractional part of the divisor. For example, $7 \div 2$ can be solved as 3 with a remainder of 1 or as $3\frac{1}{2}$.

   a) Write one word problem where the answer is 3 with a remainder of 1 and another where the answer is $3\frac{1}{2}$.

   b) How does this relate to division of fractions? Use $\frac{7}{8} \div \frac{1}{4}$ as an example.

9. The path around the local park is $1\frac{2}{5}$ miles around.

   a) How many times should Beau walk around the park if he wants to walk 5 miles?

   b) Explain the fractional part of your answer.

10. Write a word problem that can be solved by each of the following. Then solve using an algorithm of your choice.

    a) $\frac{2}{3} \div \frac{1}{4}$

    b) $\frac{2}{3} \div \frac{3}{4}$

    c) $1\frac{1}{3} \div \frac{3}{4}$

    d) Draw a diagram to illustrate one of your solutions.

    e) How do your answers to Parts a and b compare? Explain.

    f) How do your answers to Parts b and c compare? Explain.

**Think Beyond**

11. Can you divide straight across without first changing fractions to a common denominator?

    Use the following examples:

    a) $n = \frac{3}{4} \div \frac{1}{2}$

    b) $\frac{6}{15} \div \frac{3}{5} = n$

    c) $n = \frac{5}{8} \div \frac{3}{4}$

    d) $\frac{a}{b} \div \frac{c}{d} = n$

12. A store bin held 250 potatoes. $\frac{3}{5}$ of these were sold. Mr. Jackson bought $\frac{1}{10}$ of the potatoes that were left. How many potatoes did Mr. Jackson buy?

13. In the number 257,483 the value of the 5 is 5 · _____.

   **A.** 1,000

   **B.** 10,000

   **C.** 50,000

   **D.** 100,000

14. List the number at each point on the number line.

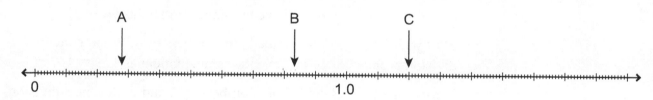

15. Round 285,785

   **a)** to the nearest ten thousand.

   **b)** to the nearest hundred.

   **c)** to the nearest hundred thousand.

Think
Beyond

16. What is the value of $n$? $5.035 = 5 + \frac{3}{n} + \frac{5}{1,000}$

17. Find the sum. $\frac{1}{100} + \frac{2}{100} + \frac{3}{100} + \ldots + \frac{97}{100} + \frac{98}{100} + \frac{99}{100}$

# Developing Fluency in Dividing Fractions and Mixed Numbers

 **Start It Off**

When Joaquim divides, he sometimes uses what he calls "double division." He divides the dividend and the divisor by the same number without changing the quotient.

For example, he says that $32 \div 8 = 16 \div 4$. He divided 32 by 2 to get 16 and divided 8 by 2 to get 4. Both division problems have the same quotient.

1. Start with $96 \div 6$ and divide both numbers by 3. What is the new division problem? Does it have the same quotient as $96 \div 6$?

2. Start with $128 \div 16$ and divide both numbers by 4. What is the new division problem? Does it have the same quotient as $128 \div 16$?

3. Start with $12 \div 4$. Divide both numbers by 8 and write a new division problem. Does it have the same quotient as $12 \div 4$?

4. Talk to a partner about why this works.

 **Hint**
See page 146

## True or False

Some statements that are true for whole numbers or counting numbers are not true for fractions, and some statements that are true for fractions are not true for whole numbers or counting numbers. Other statements are always true or always false for both types of numbers.

1. Decide whether each statement is true or false for counting numbers {1, 2, 3, . . .}. Explain using examples. Remember that we call statements false even if there is only one example for which it is not true. If a statement is true for some numbers but not others, include examples of both cases.

| Statement | True or False for Counting Numbers | Explanation and Examples |
|---|---|---|
| a) The product of two numbers is greater than or equal to the greater of the two numbers. | | |
| b) The quotient of two numbers is greater than 1 if the dividend is greater than the divisor. | | |
| c) The quotient of two numbers is less than or equal to the dividend. | | |
| d) The quotient of two numbers is less than 1 if the dividend is less than the divisor. | | |
| e) Multiplication is commutative. | | |
| f) Division is commutative. | | |

2. Work with a partner and investigate each of the statements for positive proper and improper fractions and mixed numbers. Are the answers the same for these numbers as for whole numbers? Try lots of proper and improper fractions and mixed numbers. Think about why each statement is true or false.

| Statement | True or False for Positive Fractions and Mixed Numbers | Explanation and Examples |
|---|---|---|
| a) The product of two numbers is greater than or equal to the greater of the two numbers. | | |
| b) The quotient of two numbers is greater than 1 if the dividend is greater than the divisor. | | |
| c) The quotient of two numbers is less than or equal to the dividend. | | |
| d) The quotient of two numbers is less than 1 if the dividend is less than the divisor. | | |
| e) Multiplication is commutative. | | |
| f) Division is commutative. | | |

**3.** In the Make 1 game, you use addition, subtraction, multiplication and division to write fraction expressions that simplify as close as possible to 1. After playing a few rounds of the game, talk to a partner about the strategies you use. Do your strategies depend on the operation?

## GAME · · · · · · · · · · · Make 1 · · · · · · · · · ·

**Players:** Whole class or small groups

**Materials** Squares cut out from the **Make 1** master (+, −, ×, ÷, 1, 2, 3, 3, 4, 4, 5, 5, 6, 6, 8, 12) Each player should draw the following on his or her paper.

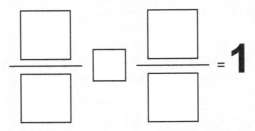

**Goal:** Get as close to 1 as possible.

**1.** The leader turns all the cards face down on the table so that the four operation cards are in pile one, the numbers 1 through 6 are in pile two and 3, 4, 5, 6, 8 and 12 are in pile three.

**2.** The leader chooses one operation card. Each player writes the operation between the two fractions.

**3.** The leader chooses one card from pile two, and each player writes the number in one of the four empty squares.

**4.** The leader chooses one card from pile three. Each player writes this number in one of the remaining three empty squares.

**5.** The leader chooses a second card from pile two, and each player writes this number in one of the two remaining empty squares.

**6.** A final card is chosen from pile three, and each player writes this number in the final empty square.

**7.** Each player simplifies the expression. The player with the answer closest to 1 is the winner and becomes the next leader. In case of a tie, choose a player who has not yet had a chance to be the leader.

**Variations:**

- After every round, each player may rearrange the numbers to try to get an answer that is even closer to 1. Anyone who can get a closer answer is the new winner.

- Change the goal from 1 to another number.

- Change the goal to the least possible number.

- Change the goal to the greatest possible number.

**4.** Suppose the four numbers chosen are 3, 4, 6 and 8.

    **a)** If the operation chosen is multiplication, what expression would have a value closest to 1?

    **b)** If the operation chosen is division, what expression would have a value closest to 1?

    **c)** Is there more than one way to get a product or quotient of 1?

    **d)** What arrangement of numbers makes the greatest possible quotient? Why?

    **e)** What arrangement of numbers makes the least possible quotient? Why?

    **f)** Give a general rule for arranging the numbers for the least possible quotient.

    **g)** Give a general rule for arranging the numbers for the greatest possible product.

 **Wrap It Up**

The product of two counting numbers other than 1 is greater than either of the two factors. The quotient of two counting numbers other than 1 is less than the dividend. This is often not true of fractions. Talk to a partner about why the product of two proper fractions is smaller than either fraction and why the quotient of two proper fractions is larger than the dividend.

 Write About It

1. To divide $1\frac{2}{3} \div \frac{3}{4}$, Dani said that she would write $1\frac{2}{3}$ as $\frac{5}{3}$ and then find $\frac{5}{3} \cdot \frac{4}{3}$. Zia said that she would also first write $1\frac{2}{3}$ as $\frac{5}{3}$. She would then write $\frac{5}{3}$ and $\frac{3}{4}$ each as twelfths, their common denominator. She would then find $\frac{20}{12} \div \frac{9}{12}$.

   a) Complete each computation. Do you get the same quotient?

   b) Compare the two methods. Which do you prefer and why?

2. Is division of fractions commutative? Explain.

3. Which of the following have quotients greater than 1? How do you know without actually dividing?

   a) $1\frac{1}{8} \div \frac{3}{4}$             c) $\frac{4}{5} \div \frac{3}{5}$

   b) $\frac{2}{3} \div \frac{3}{4}$             d) $5\frac{1}{3} \div 1\frac{2}{3}$

4. Which of the following have a quotient greater than the dividend? How do you know without actually dividing?

   a) $1\frac{1}{8} \div \frac{3}{4}$             c) $\frac{4}{5} \div \frac{3}{5}$

   b) $\frac{2}{3} \div 1\frac{3}{4}$             d) $5\frac{1}{3} \div 1\frac{2}{3}$

5. Simplify the expressions in Questions 3 and 4 using an algorithm of your choice. Show your work.

6. Use the numbers 2, 4, 6 and 8 in the squares.

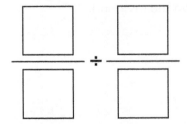

   a) Create the expression with the largest quotient.

   b) Create the expression with the smallest quotient.

7. Complete the division table. Look for patterns and try to do as few calculations as possible.

| ÷ | $\frac{1}{2}$ | $\frac{1}{4}$ | $\frac{1}{8}$ | $\frac{1}{16}$ |
|---|---|---|---|---|
| 2 | | | | |
| 1 | | | | |
| $\frac{1}{2}$ | | | | |
| $\frac{1}{4}$ | | | | |

a) What pattern do you notice across each row from left to right? Explain why this pattern happens.

b) What pattern do you notice down each column? Explain why this pattern happens.

8. In each set, estimate which expression has the greatest solution.

a) $\frac{2}{3} + \frac{1}{2}$    $\frac{2}{3} - \frac{1}{2}$    $\frac{2}{3} \cdot \frac{1}{2}$    $\frac{2}{3} \div \frac{1}{2}$

b) $\frac{2}{3} + \frac{3}{2}$    $\frac{2}{3} - \frac{3}{2}$    $\frac{2}{3} \cdot \frac{3}{2}$    $\frac{2}{3} \div \frac{3}{2}$

c) Check your estimates by computing each solution. Were your estimates correct? Why or why not?

9. Solve for $n$. Think about fact families.

a) $\frac{4}{5} \cdot n = \frac{3}{4}$

b) $n \cdot \frac{3}{5} = \frac{2}{3}$

c) $1\frac{2}{3} \div n = \frac{3}{4}$

10. Write a word problem and solve with an algorithm of your choice for each of the following. Use diagrams to illustrate your solutions.

a) $1\frac{1}{8} + \frac{1}{4}$    c) $\frac{1}{3} \cdot 1\frac{2}{3}$

b) $1\frac{2}{3} - \frac{3}{4}$    d) $1\frac{3}{5} \div \frac{2}{3}$

11. $4\frac{1}{2}$ liters of rice weighs $3\frac{3}{5}$ kilograms. How much would 1 liter of rice weigh?

12. A rectangle has an area of $\frac{3}{5}$ square foot. Its length is $\frac{3}{4}$ foot. What is the width?

13. If $n$ is a positive number, which of the following has a quotient greater than $n$? Explain.

a) $n \div \frac{3}{4}$    b) $n \div \frac{5}{3}$

**Think Beyond**

14. Combine two or more of the following fractions using addition, subtraction, multiplication and/or division: $\frac{1}{2}, \frac{1}{3}, \frac{1}{4}, \frac{1}{5}, \frac{1}{6}, \frac{1}{10}$. How many of the whole numbers from 1–10 can you form? For example, $\frac{1}{2} \cdot \frac{1}{3} \div \frac{1}{6} = 1$.

**Think Beyond**

15. Study the following:

$$\frac{2}{3} \div \frac{3}{4} = \frac{\frac{2}{3}}{\frac{3}{4}} = \frac{\frac{2}{3} \cdot \frac{4}{3}}{\frac{3}{4} \cdot \frac{4}{3}} = \frac{\frac{2}{3} \cdot \frac{4}{3}}{1} = \frac{2}{3} \cdot \frac{4}{3}$$

Use this method to show that $\frac{a}{b} \div \frac{c}{d} = \frac{a}{b} \cdot \frac{d}{c}$.

**Think Back**

16. Fill in the blanks:

   a) 18 cups = _____ quarts

   b) 40 inches = _____ feet

   c) 15 cm = _____ meters

   d) 5.2 meters = _____ cm

17. Jack bought a T-shirt and a pair of pants for $28. The pants cost $2 more than the T-shirt. How much did the T-shirt cost?

18. What fraction of the figure is shaded?

19. Find the value of each expression if $y = 6$.

   a) $3y + 7$     b) $(5y + 3) \div 3$     c) $25 - 4y$

20. This figure is made up of six identical squares. If the perimeter of the figure is 36 feet, what is the area of each square?

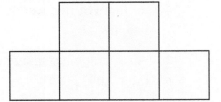

**Optional Technology Lesson for this section available in your eBook**

# Sum It Up

In this section, you extended division from whole numbers to proper and improper fractions and mixed numbers. You continued to relate division to multiplication and repeated subtraction.

## Sharing Division Problems

■ In sharing division problems, you know the total and the number of groups and you need to find the size of each group. These problems are closely related to multiplication. For example, if you have six apples to share evenly between two children, you can represent this situation with the equation $6 \div 2 = n$. You can also write this as $\frac{1}{2} \cdot 6 = n$. In this case, $n = 3$, the number of apples each child gets.

■ You might also have sharing division problems with fractions or mixed numbers as dividends and whole number as divisors. For example, if $1\frac{1}{2}$ pounds of hamburger will make three jumbo burgers and you want to find the number of pounds of hamburger in one burger, you can solve the equation $1\frac{1}{2} \div 3 = n$ or the equation $\frac{1}{3} \cdot 1\frac{1}{2} = n = \frac{1}{2}$ pound per burger.

■ In other sharing division problems, both the dividend and the divisor may be fractions or mixed numbers. For example, if $1\frac{1}{2}$ pounds of hamburger is enough for $\frac{3}{4}$ of a meatloaf, you can solve the equation $1\frac{1}{2} \div \frac{3}{4} = n$ or $\frac{4}{3} \cdot 1\frac{1}{2} = n$ to find the number of pounds of hamburger in one meatloaf.

■ Situations and diagrams can help explain why certain algorithms can be used to solve an equation. For example, the reasoning and diagrams used to solve sharing division problems can be used to explain why multiplying by the reciprocal of the divisor can be used to solve a division problem. For example, $5 \div \frac{2}{3} = n$ can be solved as $\frac{3}{2} \cdot 5 = n$. Because of the commutative property of multiplication, this might also be $5 \cdot \frac{3}{2} = n$. For any equation $\frac{a}{b} \div \frac{c}{d} = \frac{a}{b} \cdot \frac{d}{c}$ as long as $b$, $c$ and $d$ are not equal to zero. This is sometimes referred to as "invert and multiply."

## Grouping Division Problems

■ In grouping division problems, you know a total and the size of each group. You need to find the number of groups. For example, if you have six apples and want find the number of children who could each get two apples, you could solve the equation $6 \div 2 = n$. In this case, $n = 3$, the number of children who could each get two apples.

■ Grouping division problems may also have fractions or mixed numbers for the dividend and/or divisor. For example, $1\frac{4}{5} \div \frac{2}{5} = n$ can be used to represent a situation in which you have $1\frac{4}{5}$ pounds of apples and you put $\frac{2}{5}$ of a pound in each apple tart. You can make four complete tarts and would then have $\frac{1}{5}$ pound of apples left. This remainder can make $\frac{1}{2}$ of another tart.

■ The common denominator algorithm can be used to solve grouping division problems with fractions or mixed numbers. For example, to solve $1\frac{4}{5} \div \frac{2}{5} = n$, first write $1\frac{4}{5}$ as the improper fraction $\frac{9}{5}$. The expression then becomes $\frac{9}{5} \div \frac{2}{5}$. Since you already have common denominators, you divide straight across.

$$\frac{9}{5} \div \frac{2}{5} = \frac{9 \div 2}{5 \div 5}$$
$$= \frac{9 \div 2}{1} = 9 \div 2$$
$$= 4\frac{1}{2}$$

Grouping division situations are helpful in understanding the meaning of $\frac{1}{2}$. In this solution, it represents $\frac{1}{2}$ of another tart.

## Review of Algorithms for Dividing Fractions and Mixed Numbers

■ When finding the solution to a division equation involving fractions or mixed numbers, you can use either the multiply by the reciprocal of the divisor algorithm or the common denominator algorithm. For example, to solve $\frac{3}{4} \div \frac{2}{3} = n$, you can use either of these methods.

■ Multiply by the reciprocal of the divisor: $\frac{3}{4} \div \frac{2}{3} = \frac{3}{4} \cdot \frac{3}{2}$
$$= \frac{9}{8} = 1\frac{1}{8}$$

■ Common Denominator: $\frac{3}{4} \div \frac{2}{3} = \frac{9}{12} \div \frac{8}{12}$
$$= \frac{9 \div 8}{12 \div 12} = \frac{9 \div 8}{1}$$
$$= 9 \div 8 = 1\frac{1}{8}$$

### MATHEMATICALLY SPEAKING

Do you know what these mathematical terms mean?

▶ dividend        ▶ divisor        ▶ quotient

## Part 1. What did you learn?

1. Match the description with the correct expression and simplified value.

| Words | Expression | Answer |
|---|---|---|
| **a)** The number of one-fourths in three. | **e)** $3 \div \frac{1}{4}$ | **i)** 6 |
| **b)** The number in each group if there are 3 in $\frac{1}{2}$ of a group. | **f)** $\frac{1}{2} \cdot 3$ | **j)** $\frac{3}{4}$ |
| **c)** The fraction that is half of three. | **g)** $\frac{1}{4} \cdot 3$ | **k)** 12 |
| **d)** The fraction that is three times the size of one-fourth. | **h)** $3 \div \frac{1}{2}$ | **l)** $1\frac{1}{2}$ |

2. Terry needs $\frac{2}{3}$ yard string to wrap 3 packages. She will use the same amount of string for each package.

   **a)** Use a diagram to determine how much string Terry will use to wrap each package.

   **b)** Use an equation to determine how much string Terry will use to wrap each package.

3. Terry's street is $\frac{1}{4}$ mile long. Terry wants to run a total $2\frac{3}{4}$ miles.

   **a)** Use a diagram to determine how many times she must run the length of her street.

   **b)** Use an equation to determine how many times she must run the length of her street.

**4.** Sandra used $\frac{2}{3}$ cup flour to make 12 pancakes each of equal size. She wants to know how much flour goes into each pancake.

    **a)** Is this a sharing or grouping division problem? How do you know?

    **b)** Solve the problem using a model and/or equation.

**5.** Match each expression with the best estimate of its value.

| | |
|---|---|
| **a)**   $12 \div \frac{19}{40}$ | **i)**   1 |
| **b)**   $4 \cdot \frac{27}{100}$ | **ii)**   6 |
| **c)**   $\frac{11}{34} \cdot 30$ | **iii)**   24 |
| **d)**   $\frac{9}{19} \cdot 12$ | **iv)**   10 |

**6.** Write a division number sentence that fits each description.

    **a)** The dividend is any number, the divisor is a fraction and the quotient is a whole number.

    **b)** The dividend and divisor are fractions and the quotient is greater than 1.

    **c)** The dividend is a fraction, the divisor is a whole number and the quotient is less than the divisor.

**7.** Which of the expressions below simplify to a value that is greater than the dividend? How do you know?

    **a)** $\frac{3}{4} \div 3$

    **b)** $\frac{3}{4} \div \frac{1}{4}$

    **c)** $1\frac{1}{2} \div 4$

    **d)** $8 \div 16$

    **e)** $6\frac{2}{3} \div \frac{1}{3}$

**8.** Find the value of $n$ in each equation using a model or diagram. Write the value of $n$ in simplest form.

    **a)** $\frac{2}{3} \div \frac{1}{6} = n$

    **b)** $12 \div \frac{3}{4} = n$

    **c)** $6 \div 1\frac{1}{2} = n$

9. Find the value of *n* in each equation using the "invert and multiply" method and the common denominator method. Write the value of *n* in simplest form.

   **a)** $1\frac{3}{5} \div 3 = n$

   **b)** $3\frac{2}{3} \div \frac{1}{2} = n$

10. Choose one equation from Question 8 or 9 and write a sharing word problem that could be modeled using that equation.

11. Choose one equation from Question 8 or 9 and write a grouping word problem that could be modeled using that equation.

## Part 2. What went wrong?

12. Xiadon wanted to find $\frac{4}{9} \div 1\frac{1}{2}$. Here is what she did.

    $$\frac{4}{9} \div 1\frac{1}{2} = \frac{4}{9} \cdot \frac{3}{2} = \frac{2}{3}$$

    Xiadon's teacher marked her answer wrong. What could you say or do to help Xiadon find and fix her error?

13. Jordan was asked the following multiple-choice question on a recent quiz.

    > Nadia ran $6\frac{1}{2}$ miles on Monday. She ran half as far on Tuesday. Which expression could be used to find the number of miles Nadia ran on Tuesday?
    >
    > **A.** $6\frac{1}{2} \div \frac{1}{2}$        **C.** $6\frac{1}{12} \cdot 2$
    >
    > **B.** $\frac{1}{2} \cdot 6\frac{1}{2}$        **D.** $6\frac{1}{2} - \frac{1}{2}$

    Jordan chose letter A but his answer was marked wrong. Which is the correct answer choice? Why?

14. Lateisha and Don make scarves. They have 3 yards of fabric and need $\frac{2}{3}$ yard per scarf. Latiesha thinks that they can make 4 scarves with $\frac{1}{3}$ yard left over. Don thinks that they can make 4 scarves with $\frac{1}{2}$ yard left over. Who do you agree with? Why?

# Multiplying and Dividing Decimals

So far in this unit, you have explored fractions with any counting number in the denominator. In this section, we focus on decimal fractions, which have denominators that are powers of ten (10, 100, 1,000, . . .). We usually write decimal fractions in standard form, with a decimal point, rather than in fraction form. In this section, you will investigate multiplication and division with decimals. As you perform these operations, think about how these compare to multiplication and division of whole numbers as well as to multiplication and division of fractions.

 **LESSON 3.1** Making Sense of Decimal Multiplication

**MATHEMATICALLY SPEAKING**

▶ power of ten

 **Start It Off**

Complete the following and look for a pattern.

1.  $56 \times 10 =$ _____

2.  $56 \times 100 =$ _____

3.  $56 \times 1,000 =$ _____

4.  $56 \times 10,000 =$ _____

5.  Where is the decimal point in 56? What happens to the decimal point when you multiply by a power of 10?

6.  Choose another number and multiply it by increasing powers of ten. Does the same thing happen to the decimal point?

Decimals, which represent fractions with denominators that are powers of ten, were not used in English-speaking countries until the early 1600s. In the Indus River Valley, now Pakistan and India, decimal fractions were used nearly 5,000 years ago. In English-speaking countries, the decimal point is generally a dot or period (.) that separates the whole number portion from the part of the number that is less than 1. In many other countries, a comma is used instead of a dot. By the 1700s, the use of a decimal point was common in the United States. Luke found that his old math book used that notation and included problems that multiplied and divided numbers by powers of ten.

1.  Complete the following problems that Luke found in his book.

    **a)** $25,000 \div 10 =$ _____

    **b)** $25,000 \div 100 =$ _____

    **c)** $25,000 \div 1,000 =$ _____

    **d)** $25,000 \div 10,000 =$ _____

    **e)** $25,000 \div 100,000 =$ _____

    **f)** $25,000 \div 1,000,000 =$ _____

    **g)** What happens to the decimal point as you divide by increasing powers of ten?

    **h)** Which of the problems above have a quotient less than 1? How could you know without doing the computation?

**2. a)** Is $9,836 \div 100,000$ greater or less than 1? Explain.

   **b)** Write $9,836 \div 100,000$ as a fraction and as a decimal. Is it greater or less than 1?

   **c)** Use a calculator to find the quotient of $9,836 \div 100,000$. Compare your answer to Part b.

**3.** Paulo said that $0.24 \times 10 = 0.240$. Rakeem said that could not be right because $0.240 = 0.24$. Who is right? Explain using fractions and decimals.

> **Example**
>
> $0.32 \times 10$ can be written as:
>
> $0.32 \times 10 = \frac{32}{100} \times \frac{10}{1} = \frac{320}{100} = 3\frac{20}{100} = 3\frac{2}{10} = 3.2$

**4.** For each of the following, write the decimal as a fraction and multiply. Then, write the product in decimal form.

   **a)** $0.3 \times 10 = $ _____

   **b)** $4.7 \times 100 = $ _____

   **c)** $62.81 \times 10 = $ _____

   **d)** When you multiply $0.32 \times 10$, you can cancel before multiplying. $\frac{32}{\cancel{100}10} \times \frac{\cancel{10}1}{1} = \frac{32}{10} = 3.2$. Choose one of the equations in Parts a–c, and cancel before you multiply. Did you get the same product?

   **e)** What happens to the decimal point when you multiply by a power of ten? How does this compare to multiplying whole numbers by a power of ten?

**5. a)** Without calculating, what do you know about the size of $4.5 \div 0.1$ compared to $4.5 \div 1$? Discuss your answer with a partner.

   **b)** How does $4.5 \div 0.1$ compare to $4.5 \times 10$? Use fractions in your explanation.

**6.** Place the decimal point where you think it belongs in each of the following products. Check by changing the decimals to fractions and then multiplying or dividing. Delete any unnecessary zeros.

   **a)** $0.24 \times 10 = 0\,2\,4\,0\,0$

   **b)** $0.05 \times 100 = 0\,5\,0\,0\,0$

   **c)** $2.3 \div 10 = 0\,2\,3\,0\,0$

   **d)** $83.72 \div 100 = 0\,8\,3\,7\,2\,0$

7. Maylee said that if you multiply a decimal by a power of ten, you can count the zeros in the power of ten, and move the decimal point that many places to the right. Is she correct? Explain.

8. What happens to the decimal point in a number such as 6.2 when you divide by 10? When you divide by 1,000? Give two other examples using decimals. Use fractions in your explanation.

# More Multiplication of Decimals

Estimation, mental computation and justification are important skills for any mathematician.

> **Example**
>
> To mentally compute $30 \times 7$, you might say that $3 \times 7 = 21$ and 30 is $10 \times 3$. Therefore, $30 \times 7 = 10 \times (3 \times 7) = 210$.

9. Use estimation to place the decimal point in each of the following products. Add or delete zeros as necessary.

   **a)** $3 \times 7 = 0\ 2\ 1\ 0\ 0$

   **b)** $30 \times 7 = 0\ 2\ 1\ 0\ 0$

   **c)** $3 \times 70 = 0\ 2\ 1\ 0\ 0$

   **d)** $30 \times 70 = 0\ 2\ 1\ 0\ 0$

   **e)** $0.3 \times 7 = 0\ 2\ 1\ 0\ 0$

   **f)** $3 \times 0.7 = 0\ 2\ 1\ 0\ 0$

   **g)** $0.3 \times 0.7 = 0\ 2\ 1\ 0\ 0$

   **h)** $0.03 \times 7 = 0\ 2\ 1\ 0\ 0$

   **i)** $3 \times 0.07 = 0\ 2\ 1\ 0\ 0$

   **j)** What is the same about each of these problems? What is different?

   **k)** Compare your answers to a partner's. Discuss any problems where you disagree. Convert to fractions and check, if necessary.

When multiplying decimals, you could just change them to fraction form and multiply those.

> **Example**
>
> To multiply $0.4 \times 0.3$, you could just multiply $\frac{4}{10} \times \frac{3}{10}$ and get a product of $\frac{12}{100}$. You don't even have to simplify. You just write that as 0.12.

Because decimals are special fractions with denominators that are a power of ten, any problem with decimals can be written as a fraction or a mixed number.

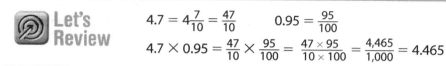

**Let's Review**

$$4.7 = 4\frac{7}{10} = \frac{47}{10} \qquad 0.95 = \frac{95}{100}$$

$$4.7 \times 0.95 = \frac{47}{10} \times \frac{95}{100} = \frac{47 \times 95}{10 \times 100} = \frac{4,465}{1,000} = 4.465$$

**10.** Using fractions, make a mental estimate of the product of $24 \times 0.76$. Multiply using fractions to check your estimate.

**11. a)** Estimate whether the product of $0.9 \times 3.1$ is greater or less than 3. Write 0.9 and 3.1 as fractions and find the product. Write your answer as a mixed number and as a decimal. Was your estimate correct?

**b)** Copy and complete the chart by first estimating the product. Check your estimate by converting the numbers to fractions and finding the product.

| Expression | Estimate of Product | Expression Written in Fraction Form | Product as a Fraction | Product as a Decimal |
|---|---|---|---|---|
| 0.05 × 18 | | | | |
| 12 × 0.95 | | | | |
| 2.1 × 10.2 | | | | |

**c)** Were your estimates close to the actual products? Why or why not?

**12.** For each of the following, write the decimals as equivalent fractions and then multiply. Do not simplify. Write your product as a decimal.

**a)** $0.7 \times 0.05$

**b)** $0.72 \times 0.4$

**c)** $0.7 \times 0.5$

**d)** $0.51 \times 0.26$

**e)** How many decimal places are there in each of the two factors? How many are there in the product? How are your answers related?

**13.** Ladonna said that to find the number of decimal places in a product, you could just add the number of decimal places in the two factors. Was she right? Explain using examples.

Raul said that he thought Ladonna was right, but when he multiplied $0.6 \times 0.5$ on his calculator, he got 0.3. He had expected an answer with two decimal places.

**14.** When 0.6 and 0.5 are written as fractions, if you do not simplify, you get $\frac{6}{10} \times \frac{5}{10} = \frac{30}{100}$.

**a)** How does this relate to the answer that Raul got on his calculator?

Use estimation and what you know about fractions to place the decimal point in each of the following products.

**b)** $6 \times 5 = 3\ 0\ 0$

**c)** $0.8 \times 5 = 4\ 0\ 0$

**d)** $4 \times 0.5 = 2\ 0\ 0$

**e)** $0.6 \times 0.5 = 0\ 3\ 0\ 0$

**f)** $0.2 \times 0.5 = 0\ 1\ 0\ 0$

**g)** Do these follow the rule of adding the number of decimal places in the two factors to find the number of decimal places in the product?

**h)** Choose one of the problems above, and explain how you could find the answer using fractions. For example, for $0.6 \times 0.5$, you might think $0.5 = \frac{1}{2}$ and $\frac{1}{2}$ of 0.6 is 0.3.

**15.** In 1878, Mr. Washington made $0.60 per hour.

**a)** How much money did Mr. Washington make in 45 minutes? In 12 minutes? In half an hour?

**b)** Write each of these as a multiplication sentence using decimals. How do you know where to put the decimal point in the product? Explain using estimation, using fractions and using your rule for multiplication of decimals.

 **Wrap It Up**

Talk to a partner about how you might use fractions to figure out where to put the decimal point when multiplying decimals.

**MATHEMATICALLY SPEAKING**

▶ power of ten

**Write About It**

1.  Grapes are sold in bags that are 0.4 pound each.

    a)  Write an equation to show the number of pounds of grapes in 6 bags.

    b)  You know that $6 \times 4 = 24$. Explain how you would estimate to find where the decimal point should go in the product of $6 \times 0.4$.

    c)  How would you use fractions to determine the placement of the decimal point?

    d)  How would you use the rule for multiplying decimals to determine the placement of the decimal point?

2.  Copy and fill in the blanks with either multiplication or division by a power of ten to get from one step to the next.

    $7{,}392 \div 100$ _____ $\longrightarrow$ 73.92 _____ _____ $\longrightarrow$ 739.2

    _____ _____ $\longrightarrow$ 0.7392 _____ _____ $\longrightarrow$ 73,920

3.  Fill in the blanks.

    a)  $64.93 \times 100 =$ _____

    b)  $23.987 \div 10 =$ _____

    c)  $489.3 \div$ _____ $= 4.893$

    d)  _____ $\times 85.34 = 8{,}534$

4.  Beyonce said that to multiply any number by 10, you just add a zero.

    a)  Megan said that $32.5 + 0 = 32.5$, so $32.5 \times 10 = 32.5$. What went wrong?

    b)  Beyonce said that adding a zero meant putting an extra zero at the end. Megan said that must mean that $32.5 \times 10 = 32.50$. Was she right?

    c)  Explain how Beyonce might be clearer about her rule.

    d)  What rule would you give for multiplying by 100 or 1,000?

5.  $12 \times 58 = 696$. Use estimation to place the decimal point in each of these products. Add or delete zeros, if necessary.

    a)  $1.2 \times 58 = 0\,6\,9\,6$     c)  $0.12 \times 5.8 = 0\,6\,9\,6$

    b)  $12 \times 5.8 = 0\,6\,9\,6$     d)  $120 \times 5.8 = 0\,6\,9\,6$

6. Look at the prices of a few groceries in 1878 and 2008.

| Item | Price in 1878 | Price in 2008 |
|---|---|---|
| Steak (per pound) | $0.16 | $9.87 |
| Cranberries (per quart) | $0.10 | $1.80 |
| Sugar (per pound) | $0.08 | $0.48 |
| Quart of milk | $0.05 | $0.75 |
| Whole chicken | $0.35 | $2.07 |

Compare the prices in 1878 to those in 2008. If you want to know how many times as expensive milk was in 2008 compared to 1878, you might think $0.05 \times n = $0.75, or $0.75 \div $0.05 = n$. Since 5¢ $\times$ 15 = 75¢, you know that milk was 15 times as expensive and $n = 15$.

Estimate to answer each of the following.

a) How many times as expensive were cranberries in 2008 as in 1878?

b) Was steak as much as 100 times as expensive in 2008 as it was in 1878? More than 50 times as expensive?

c) Which item was less than 5 times as expensive in 2008 as in 1878?

d) Which item was 6 times as expensive in 2008 as in 1878?

7. In 1878, how much did each of the following cost? Show your work with multiplication. Use repeated addition to check.

a) 1 gallon of milk

b) 3 whole chickens

c) 5 pounds of sugar

d) 4 pounds of steak

8. How much did each of these items cost in 2008? Show your work using multiplication.

   a) 1 gallon of cranberries

   b) 3.2 pounds of steak

   c) 1.5 pounds of sugar

   d) 0.5 gallon of milk

 **Think Beyond**

9. Is multiplication of decimals commutative? Give three examples.

10. Denzel spent 0.4 of his money on a book and a magazine. The book cost 3 times as much as the magazine. He had $36 left. How much did he spend on the book?

**Think Back**

11. The capacity of a container is 1 gallon. It has $1\frac{3}{4}$ quarts of water in it. How much more water can it hold?

12. Arrange the fractions from the least to the greatest: $\frac{3}{8}, \frac{3}{5}, \frac{3}{10}, \frac{3}{2}$. Explain your answer.

13. Solve for $n$: $3n + 8 = 29$

14. The mean of three numbers is 54. Two of the numbers are 48 and 60. What is the third number?

15. A pile of notebooks is $1\frac{1}{4}$ feet high. Each notebook is $\frac{1}{2}$ inch thick. How many notebooks are in the stack?

# More Metric Measurements

 Start It Off

Study this area model for the multiplication of 34 × 26 and compare it to finding the product with the partial products algorithm, as shown on the right.

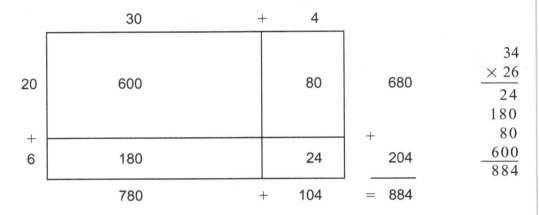

Talk to a partner about how the model works. Use an area model to find each of the following products. Check using another multiplication algorithm of your choice.

1. 98 × 73

2. 38 × 64

3. 52 × 86

 Think Beyond

4. Try the model for 748 × 69.

Estimating products of decimals is important for everyday activities. In this lesson, you will explore its uses.

The students at Sharp Middle School volunteered to help senior citizens fix up their houses. Some students learned to lay tile for bathrooms or kitchens. Their first project was to lay tile in a small rectangular area that is 0.7 m by 0.6 m. The tiles are each 10 cm by 10 cm.

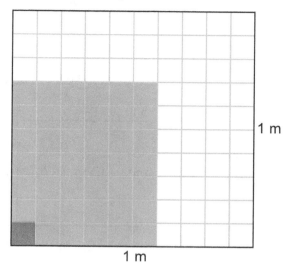

1 m

1 m

1. **a)** What are the length and width of each tile in meters?

   **b)** What is the area of one tile like the red one in the diagram in square meters?

   **c)** What is the area of the entire tiled section?

2. Use grid paper to draw tiled rectangles with the following dimensions. What is the area of each rectangle?

   **a)** 0.5 m × 0.7 m

   **b)** 0.8 m × 0.4 m

   **c)** 0.3 m × 0.9 m

When multiplying decimals, it is good to estimate first.

**MATHEMATICALLY SPEAKING**

▶ symbol "≈"

---

**Example**

To estimate the product of 2.9 and 4.1, you might think:

2.9 ≈ 3 and 4.1 ≈ 4

2.9 × 4.1 ≈ 3 × 4 or 12

The symbol ≈ stands for "approximately equal to."

After practicing on small areas, some of the students tiled entire bathrooms and kitchens.

3. For each of the following sets of floor dimensions, estimate the total area.

   a) 5.3 m × 2.5 m

   b) 3.5 m × 12.4 m

   c) 9.2 m × 10.4 m

4. Complete the diagrams and choose an algorithm for finding the total area of each space. The first one is completed for you.

a)

| | 5 m | + | 0.3 m |
|---|---|---|---|
| 2 m | 2 m × 5 m = 10 m² | | 2 m × 0.3 m = 0.6 m² |
| + 0.5 m | 0.5 m × 5 m = 2.5 m² | | 0.5 m × 0.3 m = 0.15 m² |

$$\begin{array}{r} 5.3 \\ \times\ 2.5 \\ \hline .15 \\ 2.50 \\ .60 \\ \underline{10.00} \\ 13.25 \end{array}$$

b)

| | 3 m | + | 0.5 m |
|---|---|---|---|
| 12 m | 12 m × 3 m = _____ m² | | 12 m × 0.5 m = _____ m² |
| + 0.4 m | 0.4 m × 3 m = _____ m² | | 0.4 m × 0.5 m = _____ m² |

$$\begin{array}{r} 12.4 \\ \times\ 3.5 \\ \hline \end{array}$$

c)

| | 9 m | + | 0.2 m |
|---|---|---|---|
| 10 m | | | |
| + 0.4 m | | | |

$$\begin{array}{r} 10.4 \\ \times\ 9.2 \\ \hline \end{array}$$

**5. a)** How does $53 \times 25$ compare to $5.3 \times 2.5$?

**b)** Describe an algorithm you could use to find the product of $5.3 \times 2.5$.

**6.** Use your algorithm to find the rectangles with the given dimensions. Estimate to determine if your answers make sense. Use a calculator to check, if necessary.

**a)** 43.4 m $\times$ 64.2 m

**b)** 13.1 miles $\times$ 8.3 miles

**c)** 69.1 km $\times$ 4.95 km

**7.** What is the area of a rectangle that is 1.2 m $\times$ 0.8 m? How do the areas of each of the following compare to this rectangle?

**a)** 0.6 m $\times$ 1.6 m

**b)** 0.12 m $\times$ 8 m

**c)** 0.3 m $\times$ 3.2 m

**d)** Give the dimensions of another rectangle with the same area.

**e)** Explain how you know these have the same area without completing the multiplication.

 **W**rap It Up

**MATHEMATICALLY SPEAKING**

▶ symbol "≈"

Talk to a partner about how a model for finding the area of a 25 m $\times$ 36 m rectangle is similar to a model for a 2.5 m $\times$ 3.6 m rectangle. How is it different?

 **Write About It**

1. Quanda said that to multiply $6.3 \times 8.2$, you could take $6 \times 8$ and add that to $0.3 \times 0.2$. Was she correct? Explain.

2. Use estimation to put the decimal point in the correct place in each product.

   **a)** $5.98 \times 25.6 = 1\ 5\ 3\ 0\ 8\ 8$

   **b)** $8.65 \times 9.42 = 8\ 1\ 4\ 8\ 3$

   **c)** $72.4 \times 84.25 = 6\ 0\ 9\ 9\ 7$

   **d)** Could you add the number of decimal places in the two factors to get the number of decimal places in the product? Why or why not?

3. Fill in the blanks and put a decimal point where needed to complete the multiplication.

   **a)**
   ```
          3 6 □ . 1
       ×    0 . 4 □
       ─────────────
          2 5 □ 5 7
     + □ 4 6 0 □ 0
       ─────────────
       1 □ 1 5 □ □
   ```

   **b)**
   ```
           4 2 . 1 □
       ×       □ . 7
       ─────────────
         2 □ 5 □ 2
       2 1 □ 8 0 0
       ─────────────
     □ 4 0 3 1 2
   ```

4. The area of a rectangle is $7.2 \text{ m}^2$. Give three different pairs of numbers that might be the length and the width of this rectangle.

5. Is multiplication of decimals associative? Give two examples.

**6.** Find the area of each of the following.

**Hint**
See page 146.

**a)**

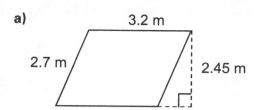

**b)**

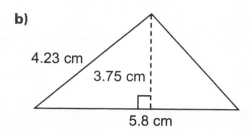

**c)**

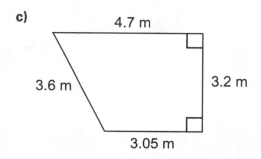

**7.** 1 in. ≈ 2.54 cm. How many centimeters are there in each of the following?

   **a)** 1.5 inches

   **b)** 3.2 inches

   **c)** 1.5 feet

**8.** 1 m ≈ 39.37 in. How many inches are there in each of the following?

   **a)** 4.5 m

   **b)** 3.25 m

   **c)** 38.2 m

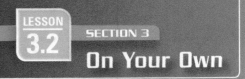

Think
Beyond

9. Each of the following shapes has the same area as the 2.5 m × 6.3 m rectangle shown below. Find the length of *n* in each shape.

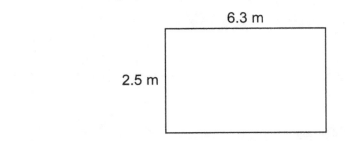

6.3 m

2.5 m

**a)**

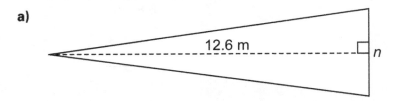

12.6 m

*n*

**b)**

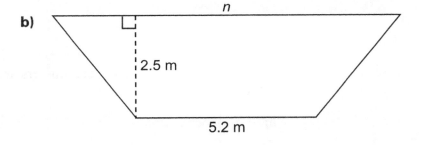

*n*

2.5 m

5.2 m

Think
Back

10. Two angles in a triangle measure 42.7° and 94.6°. What is the measure of the third angle?

   **?** **Hint**
   See page 146.

11. Solve for $n$.

   a) $5n + 7 = 52$

   b) $\frac{n}{7} + 4 = 8$

   c) $14 = 3n - 6$

12. Use mental math to compute.

   a) $\$5.97 + \$23.92$

   b) $\frac{2}{3}$ of 48

   c) $1\frac{3}{4} + \frac{5}{8}$

   d) $\$15.46 - \$7.52$

13. List the prime factors of each number. Find the greatest common divisor and the least common multiple for each pair.

   a) 18 and 45

   b) 36 and 20

   c) 15 and 50

14. Write as a decimal: $59 + \frac{3}{1,000} + \frac{5}{10}$.

 Start It Off

24 × ___ =

Fill in the blank with a whole number or decimal so that the product is

1. greater than 50

2. less than 10

3. less than 1

4. between 50 and 60

5. between 0.5 and 1.0

6. Compare your answers with a partner. Do you have the same responses? Are you both right?

A deeper understanding of decimal multiplication is important for making wise decisions about money. In this lesson, you will explore this further.

## Trip Planning

The Highlands Middle School Social Studies Club is planning to follow the Underground Railroad. The forty students need to plan their expenses. Their bus can travel 12 miles per gallon of diesel fuel. The trip will be about 156 miles. Diesel fuel costs $3.299 per gallon.

1. What is the meaning of $3.299? What does the 9 in the thousandths place mean?

2. If the students pay $2 apiece for the trip, will that be enough to pay for the diesel fuel for the bus? Talk to a partner about your reasoning.

3. The first stop is about 45 miles away. If they travel at an average of 36.5 miles per hour and leave at 8:45 am, will they get there by 10 am? Show your solution using a multiplication algorithm of your choice.

**? Hint**
See page 146.

4. Jayshawn wants to buy 1.2 pounds of trail mix for the trip. It costs $3.76 per pound.

   a) He has $4.00. Estimate to determine if he will have enough money. Justify your answer.

   b) If there is no tax, how much will 1.2 pounds cost? Show your work.

5. Some students plan to continue to Canada with their parents. Suppose that 1 U.S. dollar is worth 1.053 Canadian dollars. How many Canadian dollars would they get for $595.95?

6. Create your own problems involving multiplication of decimals and trade them with a partner. Do you get the same answer?

 **W**rap It Up

Describe an algorithm for multiplying any two decimals. Give two examples to show how your algorithm works.

**Write About It**

1. Explain why you do not have to line up the decimal points when multiplying two decimals.

2. **a)** Find two numbers whose product is 195.

   **b)** Find two numbers whose product is 19.5.

   **c)** Find two numbers whose product is 1.95.

   **d)** Explain your strategy for Parts b and c.

3. Deion's calculator is broken. It no longer displays decimal points.

   **a)** The display shows 245. List two numbers between 1 and 25 that this might represent.

   **b)** When Deion enters $24.5 \times 82.2$, the product is shown as 20139. Deion said he used $100 \times 82.2$ to help him estimate the answer. What might he do next? Where should Deion place the decimal point? Explain.

   **c)** Maria said that Deion could just use the rule to add the number of decimal places in the two factors to get the number of decimal places in the product. Where would Maria put the decimal point? Is she right?

4. On a recent national exam, only 16% of the 13-year-olds answered the following question correctly. What is the correct answer? Explain.

   Estimate: $0.3837 \times 0.22$

   **A.** 0.008

   **B.** 0.08

   **C.** 0.8

   **D.** 8.0

5. A 75-watt bulb uses 0.075 kilowatt-hour (kWh) per hour. In 2006, the average cost of 1 kWh was $0.0986.

   a) The average person in the United States used 888 kWh per month. How much would this cost?

   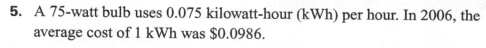
   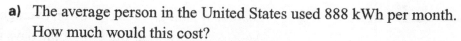

   b) What would it cost if you left ten 75-watt lightbulbs on 24 hours per day for all of December? For an entire year?

   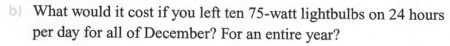
   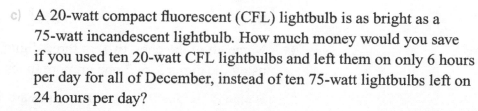

   c) A 20-watt compact fluorescent (CFL) lightbulb is as bright as a 75-watt incandescent lightbulb. How much money would you save if you used ten 20-watt CFL lightbulbs and left them on only 6 hours per day for all of December, instead of ten 75-watt lightbulbs left on 24 hours per day?

6. Mia makes time and a half for working overtime. That means that she makes 1.5 times her regular salary of $7.85 for each hour of work over 40 hours in a week. How much will she make in 1 hour of overtime?

7. Find the value of $n$.

   a) $0.8 \times n = 7.2$

   b) $n = 8.4 \times 3.25$

   c) $4.21 \times 3 = n$

8. Which of the following has the greatest product?

   A. $3.89 \times 56.8$

   B. $38.9 \times 5.68$

   C. $38.9 \times 56.8$

   D. $389 \times 0.568$

9. Estimate the product of $7.32 \times 0.48$. Which of the following statements is false?

   A. The product is greater than 0.48.

   B. The product is less than 7.32.

   C. The product is between 3 and 4.

   D. The product is less than both numbers.

Think
Back

10. Seattle, Washington, is cloudy an average of 226 days per year. Approximately what fraction of the days per year are not cloudy in Seattle?

**A.** $\frac{1}{2}$          **C.** $\frac{2}{5}$

**B.** $\frac{2}{3}$          **D.** $\frac{2}{9}$

11. Name all of the one-, two- or three-digit prime numbers you can make using the digits 3, 5, 7 one or more times each.

12. Bananas are $0.49 per pound, grapes are $2.99 per pound, and apples are $1.59 per pound. Arrange the following in order from least expensive to most expensive:

   **a)** 10 pounds of bananas

   **b)** 3 pounds of apples

   **c)** 1 pound of grapes and 1 pound of apples

13. If you double the length and width of a rectangle,

   **a)** what happens to the perimeter?

   **b)** what happens to the area?

14. Which fraction does not belong with the others: $\frac{2}{8}$, $\frac{3}{12}$, 0.25, $\frac{5}{15}$? Explain.

# Dividing Decimals

## Start It Off

> Without calculating, what do you know about 4.5 ÷ 0.95? Think about what you know about dividing fractions and the relationship of fractions to decimals. Discuss your answers with a partner.

Division of decimals is closely linked to multiplication and subtraction of decimals, as well as division of fractions and mixed numbers. In this lesson, you will continue thinking like a mathematician as you build on these connections.

## Making Sense of Decimal Division

You know that the bar in a fraction can also be thought of as division.

$\frac{1}{4} = 1 \div 4$, $\frac{1}{4} = 4\overline{)1}$ and $\frac{1}{4} = 0.25$

Money is helpful in understanding division of decimals.

**1.** In Luke's book from 1878, money was sometimes written as a fraction.

   **a)** Complete the table with money written as a fraction, mixed number or decimal.

| Money as a Fraction or Mixed Number in Simplest Form | Money with a Decimal |
|---|---|
| $3\frac{3}{4}$ | |
| | $5.40 |
| | $25.35 |
| $\frac{2}{5}$ | |

   **b)** $\frac{1}{4} = 0.25$. How might you think of the division $4\overline{)1.00}$ in terms of money?

   **c)** How is $4\overline{)100}$ related to $4\overline{)1.00}$? Discuss your answer with a partner.

   **d)** Use long division to convert $\frac{2}{5}$ to a decimal and compare the decimal to the one in your chart in Part a.

   **e)** How might you solve $2 \div 0.5$ or $0.5\overline{)2.00}$? Think about fractions or money.

   **f)** Think about the number of halves in 2. How does that relate to the problem in Part e?

   **g)** $2 \div 0.5$ as a fraction is $\frac{2}{0.5}$. What can you multiply the numerator and denominator by to get a whole number denominator?

2. Talk to a partner about how the problems in each pair are alike and how they are different.

   a) $2.1 \div 0.3$ and $21 \div 3$

   b) $1.25 \div 2.5$ and $125 \div 250$

3. Write each of the following division problems as an equivalent problem with a whole number divisor by multiplying the dividend and the divisor by the same power of ten. Write the quotient as a decimal.

   For example: $4.2 \div 0.5 = 42 \div 5 = 8.4$

   a) $0.7 \div 0.2$

   b) $0.64 \div 0.4$

   c) $3.1 \div 0.12$

   d) Write each of the division problems above as the quotient of fractions with a common denominator and solve using the common denominator algorithm. Write the quotient as a decimal. For example:

   $$4.2 \div 0.5 = \frac{42}{10} \div \frac{5}{10} = \frac{42 \div 5}{10 \div 10} = 42 \div 5 = \frac{42}{5} = 8\frac{2}{5} = 8.4$$

   e) Compare the answers you got using the two division methods. Did you get the same answer each time? Which method do you prefer? Why?

4. a) Without a calculator, solve $34\overline{)3{,}196}$.

   b) What if you bought 34 snacks for $31.96? How much does each snack cost? Explain using the quotient from $34\overline{)3{,}196}$.

   c) What if snacks are $0.34 each? How many can you buy for $31.96? Explain.

5. $27 \times 36 = 972$. Use this product and mental calculation to solve each of the following:

   a) $972 \div 3.6$

   b) $9.72 \div 0.27$

   c) $97.2 \div 36$

   d) Write a division equation with a quotient of $0.36$.

   e) Choose one of these problems and explain how you found the answer. Compare your work with a partner.

Sometimes when you divide whole numbers, you get a remainder. If you do not wish to leave the answer with a remainder, you can add a decimal point and zeros and keep dividing. For example, if you buy 4 notebooks for $15 and each costs the same, you might write $15 \div 4$ to find the cost of each. You might write this:

$$
\begin{array}{r}
3.75 \\
4\overline{)15.00} \\
-12.00 \\
\hline
3.00 \\
-2.80 \\
\hline
.20 \\
-.20 \\
\hline
0
\end{array}
$$

If, instead, you are buying bananas for $0.40 per pound and want to know how many pounds you can buy for $1.50, you might write $0.4\overline{)1.50}$. You can rewrite this with a whole number divisor by multiplying the divisor and the dividend each by 10, as $4\overline{)15}$.

Note that this gives the same answer as the problem with the notebooks. We can write $0.4\overline{)1.50} = \dfrac{1.50}{0.4} = \dfrac{1.50}{0.4} \times \dfrac{10}{10} = \dfrac{15.0}{4} = 4\overline{)15.0} = 4\overline{)15.00} = 3.75$

6.  Use long division to find each of the following quotients as a decimal. Make the divisor a whole number and annex a decimal point and zeros as necessary in the dividend to form an equivalent division problem. You might use the banana problem as an example.

    a)  $5\overline{)82}$

    b)  $0.8\overline{)47.2}$

    c)  $3.2\overline{)40}$

    d)  Choose one of these and write the division using fractions. Solve and compare your answers.

7.  For $3\overline{)2}$, what happens when you annex a decimal point and zeros? A decimal that does not end, but repeats in a pattern, is called a **repeating decimal**. How does this compare to converting the fraction $\frac{2}{3}$ to a decimal?

On the Underground Railroad trip, the Social Studies Club noted that they often used decimals.

- The bus traveled 234.5 miles in 4 hours.

- A pound of nuts cost $3.86.

- A car got 23.4 miles per gallon, and gas cost $3.159 per gallon.

- The bus got 12 miles per gallon and diesel fuel cost $3.299 per gallon.

- The club paid $10.32 for cheese that was marked $3.95 per pound.

Use your estimation skills and knowledge of operations with fractions and decimals to answer the following.

8. Did the club buy more than 3 pounds of cheese? Explain your reasoning.

9. Estimate whether the bus averaged more than 60 miles per hour. Calculate the average speed of the bus. Show your work.

10. Did the nuts cost more than $0.25 per ounce? Use mental math to find the answer.

11. Ask your own division questions about the trip. You may add other details if you wish. Trade questions with a partner. Did you get the same answers? Did you use the same methods to solve the problems? Discuss any differences.

12. Choose one of the division questions you wrote and explain the meaning of the dividend, the divisor and the quotient.

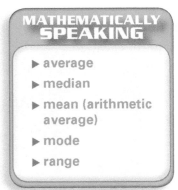

**MATHEMATICALLY SPEAKING**

- ▶ average
- ▶ median
- ▶ mean (arithmetic average)
- ▶ mode
- ▶ range

**Let's Review**

An average is one number that represents a typical value in a set of data. The median, mean, and mode are all types of averages. The median is the number that is exactly in the middle of the data set when the data points are arranged in order from least to greatest. Another average that is often used is the mean. The mean is also called the arithmetic average. To find the mean, you find the sum of all the values in the data set and then divide by the number of values. The most frequent value in a data set is the mode. The range is the difference between the greatest and the least values in a data set.

Example

The Social Studies Club priced bananas for the trip at several stores and plotted their findings using a line plot.

**Price Per Pound for Bananas**

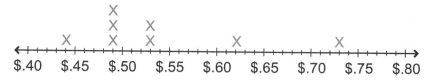

**Range:** $.73 − $.44 = $.29

**Mode:** $0.49

**Median:** List points in order: $0.44, $0.49, $0.49, $0.49, $0.53, $0.53, $0.62, $0.73. Since there are eight points, the median is the mean of the two middle values, $0.49 and $0.53. The sum of $0.49 and $0.53 is $1.02 and the median is $1.02 ÷ 2 or $0.51, the number halfway between the two middle numbers.

**Mean:** Add the values and divide by 8. $0.44 + $0.49 + $0.49 + $0.49 + $0.53 + $0.53 + $0.62 + $0.73 = $4.32. $4.32 ÷ 8 = $0.58. The mean is $0.58.

13. The club found the following prices for boxes of crackers.

| $2.87 | $2.93 | $2.82 | $2.79 | $2.80 |
|-------|-------|-------|-------|-------|
| $2.82 | $2.95 | $2.83 | $2.77 | $2.82 |

a) Plot the prices on a line plot.

b) Find the mean, median, mode and range of the prices.

## Wrap It Up

Describe an algorithm for dividing decimals that converts a division problem with a decimal divisor to an equivalent one with a whole number divisor. Give examples to show how your algorithm works.

MATHEMATICALLY
SPEAKING

▶ average

▶ line plot

▶ mean

▶ median

▶ mode

▶ range

▶ repeating decimal

Write
About It

1. You paid $8.19 for 2.1 pounds of cheese. You know that $39 \times 21 = 819$.

   a) Explain how you would use estimation and mental math to find the price of 1 pound of cheese.

   b) Explain how you would use an algorithm for division of decimals to find the price of 1 pound of cheese.

2. Lisa said that $25 \div 4 = 6.1$. What went wrong?

3. Solve the following by converting the problems to division of fractions with a common denominator. Write your answer as a decimal. For example, for $0.25 \div 0.5$, you might write:

   $$\frac{25}{100} \div \frac{50}{100} = \frac{25 \div 50}{100 \div 100} = \frac{25 \div 50}{1} = \frac{25}{50} = \frac{1}{2} = 0.5$$

   a) $8.42 \div 0.4$

   b) $0.72 \div 0.08$

   c) $1.6 \div 0.2$

   d) Choose one of the expressions above and write a word problem that this expression might be used to solve. Explain the meaning of the dividend, the divisor and the quotient in your problem.

4. Solve the problems in Question 3 by converting each one to an equivalent division problem with a whole number divisor. Show your work.

5. Use long division to find each of the following quotients as a decimal with no remainder, if possible. Multiply the divisor and the dividend by the same number to form an equivalent division problem with a whole number divisor, if necessary.

   a) $4.2\overline{)84}$

   b) $1.8\overline{)17.28}$

   c) $3\overline{)40}$

   d) Choose one of these and write the division using fractions. Solve and compare your answer to the one you got with long division.

   e) Do any of these have a quotient that is a repeating decimal? Explain.

6. Solve each of the following using an algorithm of your choice.

   a) $3.5\overline{)245}$

   b) $0.35\overline{)24.5}$

   c) $35\overline{)2{,}450}$

   d) Write another division problem that belongs with this group.

7. Do all these problems have the same quotient? Why or why not?

   a) $0.67\overline{)95.4}$

   b) $6.7\overline{)9.54}$

   c) $67\overline{)954}$

8. Without calculating, list two things that you know about $n$ in each of the following:

   a) $87 \div 0.95 = n$

   b) $14.2 \div 1.1 = n$

   c) $523 \div 0.52 = n$

   d) Choose one of the equations, and write a word problem that it could be used to solve. Solve for $n$.

9. On a recent national exam, only 7% of the 13-year-olds answered this correctly. What is the correct answer? Explain using mental math.

   Estimate: $317 \div 30$

   A. 0.01          C. 1.0

   B. 0.1           D. 10.0

10. On a recent national exam, 25% of the 13-year-olds answered this correctly. What is the correct answer? Explain using division of fractions.

    Estimate: $250 \div 0.5$

    A. 50           C. 1,000

    B. 500          D. 1,250

**11.** On a recent national exam, 19% of the 13-year-olds answered this correctly. What is the correct answer? Explain using multiplication of decimals.

Estimate: $0.239 \div 0.4$

**A.** 0.006

**C.** 0.6

**B.** 0.06

**D.** 6.0

**12.** Use mental math to fill in each blank with $<$, $>$ or $=$.

**a)** $24.8 \div 1.2$ _____ 24.8

**b)** $0.83 \div 0.5$ _____ 1.6

**c)** $1.36 \div 0.05$ _____ 20

**d)** $79.3 \div 9.1$ _____ 8

**13.** Ann Marie had the following scores on her ten-point math quizzes:

| 8 | 9 | 10 | 7 | 9 | 10 |
|---|---|----|---|---|----|
| 9 | 4 | 8  | 9 | 5 | 7  |

**a)** Plot her scores on a line plot.

**b)** Find the mean, median, mode and range of the scores.

14. The perimeter of a rectangular garden is 11.4 meters.

**a)** If the length of the garden is 3.2 meters, what is the area?

**b)** What if the perimeter stays the same, but the length of the garden changes to 4 meters? Does the area change? Explain.

**? Hint**
See page 146.

Think
Back

15. **a)** Name all the factors of 24.

**b)** Name three multiples of 24.

**c)** Name a number that is both a factor of 24 and a multiple of 24.

16. Mark and label a dot on the number line for each fraction or decimal.

$\frac{2}{6}$, $\frac{3}{4}$, 0.25, $\frac{5}{8}$, 0.125

17. Draw all the lines of symmetry in the following:

**a)**
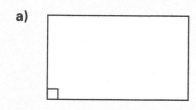

**b)**
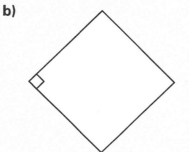

**c)**
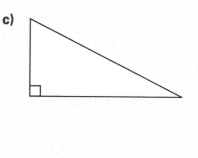

**Think Back**

18. $n!$, read "$n$ factorial," is the product of all the whole numbers from 1 through $n$. For example, 5! is $1 \times 2 \times 3 \times 4 \times 5$. So, $5! = 120$. Without multiplying, what is the digit in the ones place of 8!?

19. A shape is chosen at random from the following. What is the probability that the shape is a rectangle?

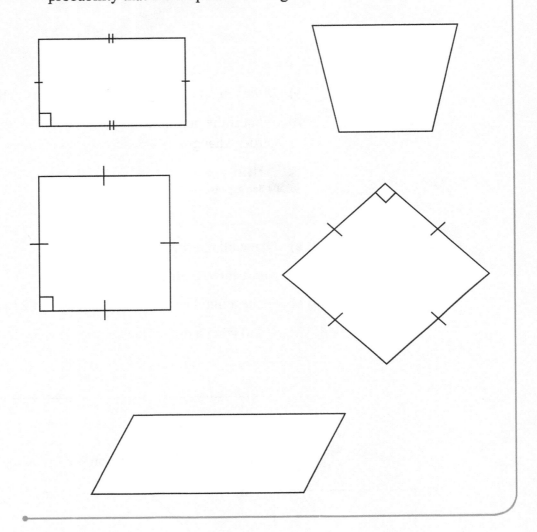

# Strengthening Rational Number Connections

➡️ **Start It Off**

Use estimation to decide which problem in each pair has the greater quotient.

1. $12.3 \div 4.5$ or $1.23 \div 4.5$

2. $1.23 \div 4.5$ or $1.23 \div 0.45$

3. Use fractions or a calculator to check your estimates. Were you correct? Why or why not?

You may have played Tic-Tac-Toe since you were young. Below you will play a variation of this familiar game, which requires you to use your estimation skills and what you know about multiplying decimals.

 · · · · · · · Decimal Tic-Tac-Toe · · · · · · · ·

**Players:** 2 (or 2 teams)

**Goal:** Get three in a row.

**Materials:** Decimal Tic-Tac-Toe board and calculator (optional)

**DIRECTIONS:**

1. One player or team chooses X and the other O.

2. The game is played on the following Tic-Tac-Toe board. This can be drawn on the board if the class is playing in two teams or on paper for each pair of students.

| 4.51 | 0.00 | 0.02 |
|------|------|------|
| 11.76 | 0.49 | 0.55 |
| 0.21 | 1.44 | 0.06 |

3. Write the following numbers where all players can see them:

    9.8          0.46          1.2          0.05

4. The player with X selects two numbers from the list, or selects the same number twice, and multiplies them. The X is placed on the board in the space that has the product rounded to the nearest hundredth. Numbers may be multiplied using either paper and pencil or a calculator, but should not be multiplied until after they have been selected by one of the players. If the product is not on the board, that player loses the turn.

5. The player with O then takes a turn. Again, two numbers are selected and multiplied, and an O is placed on the square that has the product rounded to the nearest hundredth.

6. Players take turns until one player has three Xs or three Os in a row. That player is the winner.

After playing Decimal Tic-Tac-Toe, some students discussed their strategies for selecting numbers.

1. Steve said he uses benchmarks when multiplying and dividing decimals. For example, 9.8 is close to 10. He estimates the product by multiplying by 10 and then looking for a product that is a bit smaller. Choose two of the other numbers from this game and explain how you might use benchmarks to estimate the product.

2. If Jamar picks 9.8 and 1.2, which number is he trying to match as the product? Explain your reasoning.

3. Misha wants a product of 0.49 because she likes to get the middle number. Which two numbers should she choose? Why?

4. One of the possible products is not on the board. Without multiplying all the possible combinations of numbers, can you determine which product is missing? Explain.

5. Choose four new decimals and make a new Decimal Tic-Tac-Toe board. Think about benchmarks when you choose your decimals. How do you find the products to put on the board? Trade boards with another pair of students and play each other's games. Discuss the strategies that you use.

6. Choose four or five fractions or mixed numbers and make a new Decimal Tic-Tac-Toe board. Compare the strategies that you used for a game with fractions or mixed numbers to the strategies that you used for a game with decimals.

In the Target Game, you will continue to use estimation and knowledge of decimal, fraction and mixed number multiplication.

---

## GAME · · · · · · · · Target Game · · · · · · · ·

**Players:** 2 (or 2 teams)

**Goal:** Find a missing multiplier to get a given product.

**Materials:** Calculator and 2 Target Game sheets

**DIRECTIONS:**

1. Players choose one of the columns on the Target Game sheet. The player whose birthday is the closest to today's date is Player A and the other player is Player B. (In teams of 2, the team with the player with the closest birthday is Team A.) Player A chooses a number to put in the blank and uses the calculator to multiply. For example, if the problem is $16 \times \underline{\quad} = 148$, Player A may guess 9 and write $16 \times 9 = 144$ for Trial 1. Both players should record this guess on their game sheets.

2. Player B then guesses a new number. In this case, Player B should realize that a larger guess is needed and might try 9.1. Both players would then write $16 \times 9.1 = 145.6$ for Trial 2.

3. Players take turns until one player guesses the right number. Record the winner for the round at the bottom of the column.

4. The player with the most wins at the end of the game is the winner.

---

7. You have the equation $15 \times \underline{\quad\quad} = 96$. Your opponent guessed 6 and wrote $15 \times 6 = 90$. You know that you need 6 more and you know that $15 \times 4 = 60$. What should you guess? Explain.

8. Ben has the equation $2\frac{2}{3} \times \underline{\quad\quad} = 12$. His opponent guessed 5 and wrote $2\frac{2}{3} \times 5 = 13\frac{1}{3}$. Ben notices that this is $1\frac{1}{3}$ more than he needs. What should he guess? Why?

9. Work with a partner to make up your own Decimal Target Game. Trade with another pair and play. Discuss your strategies.

## Wrap It Up

You know that $35 \times 8 = 280$ and $35 \times 9 = 315$. Talk to a partner about how you might use mental computation to determine the missing number in $35 \times$ _____ $= 294$.

**Write About It**

1. You are playing Decimal Tic-Tac-Toe and want to get a product of 5.15 rounded to the nearest hundredth. You have to choose two numbers from 0.52, 9.9, 4.8 and 0.049. Which two numbers should you choose? Explain your choice.

2. Draw an area model to show each of the following. Write an equation to show the product.

   **a)** $\frac{2}{3} \times \frac{3}{4}$     **b)** $0.5 \times 1.2$     **c)** $1\frac{1}{2} \times \frac{3}{5}$

3. Find $n$ for each. Show your work.

   **a)** $4\frac{1}{2} - 1\frac{3}{5} = n$     **b)** $n - 1\frac{3}{4} = 6\frac{5}{8}$     **c)** $9.23 \times n = 59.7$

4. Write a word problem that could be solved by each of the following. Include the solution and show your work using words, equations and/or diagrams.

   **a)** $6\frac{5}{6} + 2\frac{3}{4}$     **b)** $3.25 \times 4.1$     **c)** $89.3 \div 2.1$

5. **a)** For each of the following, the same operation was performed on each input to get the output. Find the operation and complete the chart.

   | Input | Output |
   |-------|--------|
   | 0.25 | 0.05 |
   | 20.5 | 4.1 |
   | $\frac{3}{20}$ | 0.03 |
   | 4.8 | $\frac{24}{25}$ |
   |  | 3.5 |
   | 3.1 |  |

   **b)** The operation is _____ .

6. Complete the following multiplication table where each number at the top is multiplied by the number at the left. Show your work. (Do not use a calculator.)

   | × | 4.2 | 0.4 |  |
   |---|-----|-----|-----|
   | 16.7 |  |  | 20.04 |
   | 0.9 |  |  | 1.08 |
   | 86.1 |  |  |  |

7. Tell whether each of the following has the same product as 14.6 × 3.1.

   a) 1.46 × 31

   b) 0.31 × 146

   c) 0.146 × 31

   d) 62 × 0.73

   e) Write another expression with the same product. as 14.6 × 3.1

8. Estimate to place the decimal point in each of the following products.

   a) 57.32 × 2.1 = 1 2 0 3 7 2

   b) 7.31 × 256 = 1 8 7 1 3 6

   c) 45.2 × 3.65 = 1 6 4 9 8

   d) Choose one and explain your thinking.

9. 47.6 × 7.5 = 357. Write three other facts in the same fact family.

 **Think Beyond**

10. Select any number. Divide by 0.5. Divide your answer by 5. Multiply that answer by 2.5. What is your final answer? Explain how this works.

 **Think Back**

11. Give the reciprocal of each of the following:

    a) $2\frac{2}{3}$          b) 7          c) $\frac{9}{5}$

12. Plot the following points on a Cartesian grid.

    a) (4, 2)

    b) (8, 2)

    c) (8, 5)

    d) (4, 5)

    e) Connect the points in order and connect the last point to the first one. What shape is formed?

13. Each week, the Johnson family randomly chooses one day to go in-line skating together. What is the probability that they will choose Tuesday this week?

14. Convert each measurement to pounds.

    a) 56 ounces          b) 4.5 tons

15. What is the volume of a box that is 5" × 8" × 12"?

 **Optional Technology Lesson for this section available in your eBook**

# Sum It Up

In this section, you extended your understanding of multiplication and division to decimals. Relating multiplication and division of decimals to each other and to operations with whole numbers and fractions builds a deeper understanding.

## Multiplying Decimals

■ When you multiply a number by a power of ten, you can count the number of zeros in the power of ten and move the decimal point in the product that many places to the right. For example, $8.29 \times 1,000 = 8,290$.

■ Situations and diagrams can be used to make sense of fraction and decimal multiplication and division. For example, if you have a garden that is 6.8 meters by 9.4 meters, you might first estimate that this is about 7 meters by 9 meters or 63 square meters. To find a more exact area, you might use an area model and the distributive property.

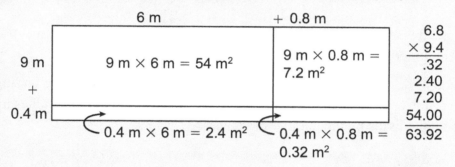

■ When you multiply two decimals, you can use the same algorithm that you use for multiplying whole numbers. To determine where the decimal point goes, use your knowledge of whole number and fraction multiplication to estimate the product. You can also add the number of decimal places in the two factors and count that number of places in the product.

For example:

$$
\begin{array}{rl}
4.5 & \text{(1 decimal place)} \\
\times\ .32 & \text{(2 decimal places)} \\
\hline
90 & \\
1350 & \\
\hline
1.440 & 2 + 1 = 3 \text{ decimal places}
\end{array}
$$

You might also think that 0.32 is a little less than $\frac{1}{3}$, and $\frac{1}{3}$ of $4\frac{1}{2}$ is $1\frac{1}{2}$. The decimal point must go between the 1 and the 4 to make the product a little less than $1\frac{1}{2}$.

# Dividing Decimals

■ When you divide a number by a power of ten, you can count the number of zeros in the divisor and move the decimal point in the dividend that many places to the left. For example, $32.76 \div 100 = 0.3276$.

■ When dividing decimals, you can use the same algorithm that you use for dividing whole numbers, but first multiply the divisor and the dividend by the same power of ten to make the divisor a whole number. To estimate where the decimal point goes in the quotient, use your knowledge of whole number and fraction division. For example, to divide 33.18 by 4.2, you might first estimate. $32 \div 4 = 8$, so the quotient should be about 8.

Note that $4.2\overline{)33.18}$ will have the same quotient as $42\overline{)331.8}$ because $4.2 \times 10 = 42$ and $33.18 \times 10 = 331.8$

$$
\begin{array}{r}
7.9 \\
42\overline{)331.8} \\
\underline{294}\phantom{.} \\
3.78 \\
\underline{3.78} \\
0
\end{array}
$$

Once the divisor is written as a whole number, you can place the decimal point of the quotient directly above the decimal point in the dividend.

■ Division of decimals can be used in a number of situations, including finding the mean of a set of data points. To find the mean, you find the sum of all the values in the data set and then divide by the number of values.

---

## MATHEMATICALLY SPEAKING

Do you know what these mathematical terms mean?

▶ average                         ▶ median                ▶ range

▶ line plot                       ▶ mode                  ▶ repeating decimal

▶ mean (arithmetic average)       ▶ power of ten          ▶ symbol "≈" (is approximately equal to)

---

# Study Guide

**Multiplying and Dividing Decimals**

## Part 1. What did you learn?

1. Each large square below has an area of 1 square unit. Find the dimensions and area of each blue rectangle.

   a.

   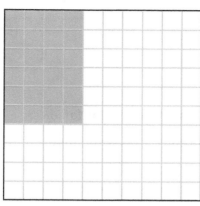

   b.

   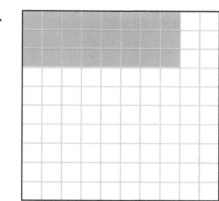

   c.

   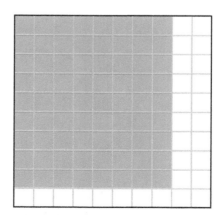

**2.** Use an area model to find the product of 3.4 × 6.2.

**3.** Choose the best estimate of each product or quotient.

| Expression | Estimate | | |
|---|---|---|---|
| **a.** 0.4 × 11.8 | 6 | 48 | 60 |
| **b.** 0.09 × 100 | $\frac{1}{100}$ | 1 | 10 |
| **c.** 16 ÷ 0.98 | $\frac{16}{100}$ | 16 | 150 |
| **d.** 0.51 ÷ 0.24 | 0.2 | 2 | 20 |

**4.** Determine whether each statement is true or false.

   **a.** Any fraction with a denominator of 6 will convert to a repeating decimal.

   **b.** The fraction $\frac{1}{8}$ converts to a repeating decimal.

   **c.** The fraction $\frac{1}{6}$ converts to a repeating decimal.

   **d.** Any fraction with a denominator of 20 will convert to a terminating decimal.

**5.** Copy and complete the equations below by filling in each pair of blanks with a multiplication or division symbol and a power of ten.

   **a.** 1,234 _____ _____ = 12.34

   **b.** 12.34 _____ _____ = 123.4

   **c.** 123.4 _____ _____ = 0.1234

   **d.** 0.1234 _____ _____ = 1.234

**6.** Compute. Show your work.

   **a.** 0.38 × 0.23　　　**c.** $0.5\overline{)52.75}$

   **b.** 4.03 × 0.6　　　**d.** $7.4\overline{)40.7}$

**7.** Jin's small fish bowl holds 0.45 liter of water. His large fish tank holds 2.4 times as much water. How much water does his large fish tank hold?

8.  Charla bought 3.5 pounds of raisins for her homemade trail mix. She puts $\frac{1}{4}$ pound of raisins in each batch of trail mix. How many batches of trail mix can Charla make with 3.5 pounds of raisins?

## Part 2. What went wrong?

9.  Jaylene's teacher asked her if the quotient of 15 ÷ 0.4 was greater than or less than 15. Jaylene said, "The quotient is less than 15 because the quotient is always less than the dividend." Jaylene's teacher told her that this was not correct. What is wrong with Jaylene's reasoning? What could you say or do to help her make an accurate prediction about the size of the quotient?

# Unit Study Guide

Fraction Times: Focusing on Multiplication and Division of Fractions and Decimals

## Part 1: What did you learn?

### SECTION 1

1. Explain to a friend who has been absent from class for a while how to do each of the following:

   a. multiply a fraction by a whole number

   b. multiply two fractions

   c. multiply two mixed numbers

2. Use what you learned about multiplying two fractions to complete the following:

   a. Write a story problem that could be solved using the expression $\frac{1}{2} \times \frac{3}{8}$.

   b. Solve your problem with an equation.

   c. Draw a diagram to match your equation.

3. You have also learned how to add two fractions.

   a. Write a story problem that could be solved using the expression $\frac{1}{2} + \frac{3}{8}$.

   b. Solve your problem with an equation.

   c. Draw a diagram to match your equation.

   d. What is the difference between the diagram you drew in Part c of this question and the diagram you drew for Part c of Question 2?

4. Solve $4 \times \frac{3}{4}$ on a number line. Label the number line and your answer. Write an addition equation that matches your diagram.

5. Louise invited some friends over to watch a movie. Her friends ate 12 small bags of popcorn. Each bag was $\frac{2}{3}$ cup. Louise bought 12 bottles of water at the store before the party. Her friends drank $\frac{2}{3}$ of them.

   a. Write an equation to show how many cups of popcorn Louise's friends ate.

   b. Use a number line or another model to show how many cups of popcorn they ate.

   c. Write an equation to show how many bottles of water Louise's friends drank.

   d. Use a number line or another model to show how many bottles of water they drank.

6. When you multiply a fraction by a whole number, can you use the same rule as when you multiply a whole number by a fraction? Why or why not?

7. How is multiplication of a fraction by a whole number like repeated addition? Use $8 \times \frac{3}{4}$ as an example and include a situation, a model and an equation in your answer. How is $8 \times \frac{3}{4}$ related to $\frac{3}{4} \times 8$? Use situations, models and equations in your explanation.

8. Find each product by simplifying the expression. An example has been provided to help you.

   $$\frac{1}{12} \times \frac{8}{9} = \frac{1 \times 8}{12 \times 9} = \frac{1 \times \cancel{8}^2}{\cancel{12}^3 \times 9} = \frac{2}{27}$$

   a. $\frac{2}{5} \times \frac{15}{16}$

   b. $5\frac{1}{4} \times 2\frac{5}{7}$

9. Copy and complete the following chart using mental math. Be prepared to explain your thinking.

| $\times$ | 6 | $\frac{1}{2}$ | 2 |
|---|---|---|---|
| $4\frac{1}{2}$ | | | |
| $12\frac{2}{3}$ | | | |
| $\frac{1}{6}$ | | | |

10. Use the numbers below to complete the riddles. You may use each number more than once.

$$\frac{2}{3} \qquad 12\frac{2}{9} \qquad 3\frac{3}{4} \qquad 4$$

   a. I multiplied _____ by $\frac{4}{9}$ and got a product that was smaller than $\frac{4}{9}$.

   b. I multiplied _____ by $\frac{4}{9}$ and got a product that was close to 6.

   c. I multiplied _____ by _____ and the product was greater than one factor but smaller than the other.

   d. I multiplied _____ and _____ and the product was a whole number.

11. Dan built a rectangular pen for his dog. The dog pen is $3\frac{2}{3}$ yards wide by $2\frac{1}{3}$ yards long. What is the area of the dog pen?

12. Is the product of two fractions that are both greater than 0 but less than 1 ever a whole number? Why or why not?

13. The equation $9 \times (2 + \frac{1}{3}) = (9 \times 2) + (9 \times \frac{1}{3})$ shows an example of the _____ property.

14. The equation $12 \times \frac{3}{4} = \frac{3}{4} \times 12$ shows an example of the _____.

15. The equation $\frac{2}{3} \times 1 = 1 \times \frac{2}{3} = \frac{2}{3}$ shows an example of the _____.

SECTION 2

16. Determine if each statement below is true or false.

   a. The reciprocal of 4 is ⁻4.

   b. The quotient of a number divided by its reciprocal is 1.

   c. The product of a number and its reciprocal is always 1.

   d. The reciprocal of $1\frac{2}{3}$ is $1\frac{3}{2}$.

17. Use estimation to find the correct simplified value of each expression.

| Expression | Simplified Value | | |
|---|---|---|---|
| **a.** $17\frac{4}{5} \div \frac{1}{10}$ | 17 | 178 | 7 |
| **b.** $\frac{5}{8} \div 1\frac{1}{4}$ | $\frac{1}{100}$ | $\frac{1}{2}$ | 2 |
| **c.** $6\frac{3}{4} \div \frac{3}{8}$ | $1\frac{3}{8}$ | 10 | 18 |

18. Write a story problem that could be modeled using one of the expressions from Question 17.

19. Nadia works at a boating supply store where people can cut their own length of rope. Her job is to take leftover pieces of rope and divide them equally into smaller pieces of rope. She must figure out the length of each piece of rope she creates. Help her by completing the following chart:

| | Total Length of Rope | Number of Pieces of Rope | Multiplication Equation to Figure out the Length of Each Small Piece of Rope | Division Equation to Figure out the Length of Each Small Piece of Rope |
|---|---|---|---|---|
| **a.** | $12\frac{3}{4}$ feet | 3 | | |
| **b.** | $8\frac{1}{2}$ feet | 4 | | |
| **c.** | $9\frac{2}{3}$ feet | 2 | | |

20. Liam takes the subway to work. Each subway token costs $2\frac{1}{4}$. He has a total of $27\frac{3}{4}$.

   a. Use a division equation to figure out how many subway tokens he can buy with $27\frac{3}{4}$. Show your work.

   b. Interpret your quotient from Part a.

21. A sporting goods clothing company uses $1\frac{5}{8}$ yards of material to make one soccer jersey. How many jerseys can be made with a total of 12 yards? Show your work.

22. Compare the values of the expressions using $=$, $<$ or $>$.

   a. $3 \div \frac{1}{4}$ _____ $3 \times 4$

   b. $2 \times \frac{2}{3}$ _____ $2 + \frac{2}{3}$

   c. $3\frac{1}{4}$ _____ $3 + \frac{1}{4}$

   d. $\frac{1}{2} \div \frac{1}{4}$ _____ $2 \times \frac{1}{4}$

23. Find the missing entries in the chart below.

| | I. Division Equation | II. Using the Common Denominator Algorithm to Find $n$ | III. Invert and Multiply Algorithm to Find $n$ | IV. Value of $n$ |
|---|---|---|---|---|
| a. | $12\frac{1}{4} \div 3 = n$ | | | |
| b. | | | $\frac{10}{4} \times \frac{2}{5} = n$ | |
| c. | $2\frac{1}{8} \div \frac{3}{4} = n$ | | | |
| d. | $\frac{1}{4} \div 3\frac{1}{2}$ or equivalent | $\frac{1}{4} \div \frac{14}{4} = n$ | | |

**SECTION 3**

24. Fill in the blanks in the paragraph below.

Matthew looked at the expression $0.4 \times 6$ and figured out that it was close to $\frac{1}{2}$ of 6. He knows that $\frac{1}{2}$ of 6 is _____. Since
$\phantom{xxxxxxxxxxxxxxxxxxxxxxxxxxx}$ 1
$0.4 \times 6$ is similar to $\frac{1}{2}$ of 6, the product of $0.4 \times 6$ must be close
to _____. He figured out that the product of $0.4 \times 6$ was
$\phantom{xxxx}$ 2
either 24, 2.4 or 0.24. Since _____ is the closet to 3, he
$\phantom{xxxxxxxxxxxxxxxxxxxxx}$ 3
figured out that _____ was the correct product.
$\phantom{xxxxxxxxxxxxx}$ 4

25. Fill in the blanks in the paragraph below.

Samantha looked at the expression $0.24 \times 7.8$. She reasoned that the
decimal 0.24 was close to the familiar fraction _____. And
$\phantom{xxxxxxxxxxxxxxxxxxxxxxxxxxxxxxxxxxxxxxx}$ 1
7.8 is close to the whole number _____. So, $0.24 \times 7.8$ is
$\phantom{xxxxxxxxxxxxxxxxxxxxxxxxxxxx}$ 2
similar to the expression _____, which has a product
$\phantom{xxxxxxxxxxxxxxxxxxxxxxxxxxx}$ 3
of 2. This means that the expression $0.24 \times 7.8$ must have a
product close to _____. Samantha knows that $0.24 \times 7.8$
$\phantom{xxxxxxxxxxxxx}$ 4
is either 1,872, 187.2, 18.72 or 1.872. Since _____ is close
$\phantom{xxxxxxxxxxxxxxxxxxxxxxxxxxxxxxxxxxxxxx}$ 5
to _____, the product must be _____.
$\phantom{xxx}$ 6 $\phantom{xxxxxxxxxxxxxxxxxxxxx}$ 7

26. The product of 5.8 and 25 is 145. Use this for each of the following.

   **a.** Find two numbers with a product of 14.5.

   **b.** Find two numbers with a product of 1.45.

   **c.** Find two numbers with a product of 0.145.

   **d.** Find two numbers with a product of 0.0145.

27. Alycia bought a combination cork/white board to help her stay organized. The board is 2.5 feet wide and 2.25 feet long.

   **a.** Sketch the board on grid paper.

   **b.** Use your sketch to find the area of the board.

   **c.** Convert the decimal dimensions to fractions. Find the area of the board using the fractions and an algorithm. Are your answers from Parts b and c equivalent?

28. Find the missing entries in the chart below.

| I. | II. | III. | IV. |
|---|---|---|---|
| Original Expression | Equivalent Expression with Fractions | Expression with Common Denominators | Quotient |
| **a.** 3.6 ÷ 0.12 | | | |
| **b.** 0.45 ÷ 0.4 | $\frac{45}{100} \div \frac{4}{10}$ | | |
| **c.** 0.16 ÷ 0.8 | | | |

29. Deena's dog, Doogle, weighs 9.1 kilograms. Her cat, Bugle, weighs 2.6 kilograms. How many times Bugle's weight is Doogle's weight?

30. Tim bought 0.6 pound of almonds. Almonds cost $3\frac{1}{4}$ per pound. How much did Tim pay for his almonds? Solve this problem using decimals. Show your work.

31. Compute. Show your work.

   **a.** 450 ÷ 0.5

   **b.** 4.8 ÷ 2.4

   **c.** 33.3 ÷ 7.4

   **d.** 2.2 ÷ 0.011

**32.** Aloysha learned how to multiply fractions by simplifying the factors. Here is what he did to multiply $\frac{5}{6} \times \frac{9}{7}$:

$$\frac{5}{6} \times \frac{9}{7} = \frac{5}{6^3} \times \frac{9^3}{7} = \frac{15}{21}$$

His teacher marked his answer wrong. Why? What could you say or do to help Aloysha find and fix his error?

**33.** Sabeen said she found a new way to multiply mixed numbers. Here is her new method:

$$2\frac{2}{3} \times 3\frac{3}{4} = (2 \times 3) + \left(\frac{2}{3} \times \frac{3}{4}\right) = 6 + \frac{2^1}{3_1} \times \frac{3^1}{4_2} = 6 + \frac{1}{2} = 6\frac{1}{2}$$

Her friend Diana used the improper fraction method and got a different answer. Here is what she did:

$$2\frac{2}{3} \times 3\frac{3}{4} = \frac{8}{3} \times \frac{15}{4} = \frac{8^2}{3_1} \times \frac{15^5}{4_1} = 10$$

Whose answer do you think is correct? Why?

**34.** On a recent quiz in Ms. Mirabile's class, many of the students chose letter C as the answer to the following multiple-choice question.

Tayra usually makes sugar cookies with a recipe that uses 2 cups of sugar. She found a new recipe that uses only $\frac{1}{4}$ as much sugar. Which expression could be used to figure out how many cups of sugar are used in this new recipe?

**A.** $\frac{1}{4} \div 2$     **C.** $2 \div \frac{1}{4}$

**B.** $\frac{1}{4} \times 2$     **D.** $2 + \frac{1}{4}$

Why would somebody choose letter C as the answer? Where is the error in their reasoning? Which is the correct choice? Why?

**35.** Tim thinks that the product of $4.50 \times 0.4$ should be 0.180 because there are a total of three decimal place values in the numbers 4.50 and 0.4. What is wrong with Tim's reasoning? How could he use estimation to help determine the correct placement of the decimal point in the product?

# Glossary

**average** One number representing a typical value in a data set. The mean, median and mode are three types of averages.

**Example**

Set $A$: $\{1, 4, 8, 15, 17\}$

The mean or arithmetic average of Set $A$ is 9; the median or center value is 8.

---

**distributive property of multiplication over addition** The property that states that to multiply a sum by a number, you can multiply each addend by the number, and then add the products.

**Example**

For numbers $a$, $b$ and $c$: $a \bullet (b + c) = ab + ac$

$3 \bullet (5 + 8) = (3 \bullet 5) + (3 \bullet 8)$

---

**dividend** The number being divided in a division problem.

**Example**

The following are forms of the division problem "twenty-three divided by five." The number 23 is the dividend.

$23 \div 5 = 4.6$

$\frac{23}{5} = 4\frac{3}{5}$

$$5\overline{)23.0} \quad 4.6$$

---

**divisor** The number that is doing the dividing in a division problem.

**Example**

The following are forms of the division problem "twenty-three divided by five." The number 5 is the divisor.

$23 \div 5 = 4.6$

$\frac{23}{5} = 4\frac{3}{5}$

$$5\overline{)23.0} \quad 4.6$$

---

**identity for multiplication (multiplicative identity)** A number that does not change any number it multiplies. The multiplicative identity is always equivalent to 1.

**Example**

For any number $a$: $a \bullet 1 = 1 \bullet a = a$.

$5 \bullet 1 = 1 \bullet 5 = 5$

$\frac{1}{2} \bullet \frac{3}{3} = \frac{3}{3} \bullet \frac{1}{2} = \frac{1}{2}$

$99.99 \bullet \frac{100}{100} = \frac{100}{100} \bullet 99.99 = 99.99$

---

**line plot** A graph that shows how often values occur in a data set along a number line. Line plots are used to graph small sets of data.

**Example**

Set $C$: $\{1, 2, 6, 4, 2, 3, 2, 4\}$

The line plot for Set $C$ is:

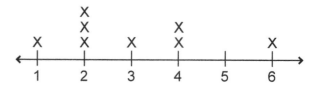

**mean (arithmetic average)** The number found by summing the numbers in a data set and dividing the sum by the number of pieces of data.

**Example**

Set $A$: $\{1, 4, 8, 15, 17\}$

Mean of Set $A$: $\dfrac{(1 + 4 + 8 + 15 + 17)}{5} = 9$

---

**median** The middle data value in an ordered data set.

**Example**

Set $A$: $\{1, 4, 8, 15, 17\}$

Median of Set $A$: 8

Set $B$: $\{-3, -1, 5, 9, 10, 20\}$

Median of Set $B$: 7

---

**mode** The number that occurs most frequently in a data set.

**Example**

Set $C$: $\{5, 8, 2, 10, 2, 8, 7, 8\}$

Mode of Set $C$: 8

---

**multiplicative inverse** A number that when multiplied by a given number results in a product of 1. The reciprocal of a number.

**Example**

For any number $a$, where $a \neq 0$, $\frac{1}{a} \cdot a = 1$

$\frac{1}{7} \cdot 7 = 1$; $\frac{1}{7}$ is the multiplicative inverse of 7, and 7 is the multiplicative inverse of $\frac{1}{7}$.

---

**power of ten** A number resulting from raising 10 to a whole number exponent.

**Example**

$10^0 = 1$

$10^1 = 10$

$10^2 = 100$

$10^3 = 1,000$

$10^4 = 10,000$

---

**product** The result of multiplying two or more numbers or expressions.

**Example**

The product of $2 \cdot 3$ is 6.

The product of $3 \cdot 4x \cdot 10y$ is $120xy$.

---

**quotient** The result of dividing one number by another; the answer to a division problem.

**Example**

The following are forms of the division problem "twenty-three divided by five." The quotient is 4.6 or $4\frac{3}{5}$.

$23 \div 5 = 4.6$

$\frac{23}{5} = 4\frac{3}{5}$

$$5 \overline{)23.0} \quad 4.6$$

**range** The difference between the greatest and the least values in a data set.

**Example**

Set $B$: $\{-3, -1, 5, 9, 10, 20\}$

Range of Set $B$: 23

---

**reciprocal** The multiplicative inverse of a number. A number multiplied by its reciprocal equals 1.

**Example**

The reciprocal of 5 is $\frac{1}{5}$.

The reciprocal of $\frac{1}{2}$ is $\frac{2}{1}$ or 2.

The reciprocal of $-\frac{5}{12}$ is $-\frac{12}{5}$.

---

**repeating decimal** A decimal that has a digit or a sequence of digits that repeats without ending.

**Example**

$\frac{1}{3} = 0.33\ldots = 0.\overline{3}$

$\frac{1}{7} = 0.142857142857\ldots = 0.\overline{142857}$

---

**symbol "≈"** Approximately equal.

**Example**

$4.9278 \approx 4.93$ is read "4.9278 is approximately equal to 4.93."

## Lesson 1.1

### On Your Own

Page 10, Question 13: One mile is 5,280 feet.

Page 10, Question 14: Draw a bar diagram.

Page 11, Question 16: Try the "guess, test, and refine" method. The number will be a whole number. Use what you know about multiples of 4 and 5.

Page 11, Question 17: Try working backwards. Use a model, with pennies or chips for the bananas.

## Lesson 1.2

### More Fraction Multiplication Models

Page 16, Question 9f: How might you write a whole number as a fraction? $5\frac{5}{?}$

## Lesson 1.5

Page 45, Question 7: Draw a bar diagram.

Page 45, Question 8: Draw a bar diagram.

## Lesson 2.1

### How Big Is Each Group?

Page 57, Question 7c: Think about an equivalent fraction with a numerator that is divisible by 4.

### On Your Own

Page 61, Question 11: Try stacking the sandwiches and making as few cuts as possible.

Page 63, Question 16: Remember that some shapes can fit several categories.

## Lesson 2.2

### Start It Off

Page 64, Question 4: Think about writing the division expression as a fraction and using the identity to write an equivalent fraction.

## Lesson 2.4

### Start It Off

Page 80, Question 4: 32 ÷ 8 can be written as $\frac{32}{8}$. Think about simplifying fractions.

## Lesson 3.2

### On Your Own

Page 107, Question 6: The area of a triangle is $\frac{1}{2}bh$. The area of a parallelogram is $bh$. The area of a trapezoid is $\frac{1}{2}(b_1 + b_2)h$.

Page 109, Question 10: The sum of the measures of the angles of a triangle is 180°.

## Lesson 3.3

### Trip Planning

Page 110, Question 3: How many hours are there between 8:45 am and 10 am? Write this as a decimal.

## Lesson 3.4

### On Your Own

Page 123, Question 14b: Find the width and then find the area.

# Index